LIFE NATURE LIBRARY

THE
SEA

OTHER BOOKS BY THE EDITORS OF LIFE:

LIFE NATURE LIBRARY

THE
SEA

by Leonard Engel
and The Editors of LIFE

TIME INCORPORATED • NEW YORK • 1961

About the Author

Leonard Engel has had a long and successful career as a free-lance writer on scientific subjects. In the past three years he has made oceanography his special province. Not content with secondhand information, Engel went to sea in the *Vema*, the famous three-masted oceanographic schooner of the Lamont Geological Observatory. He made two trips, one in the tropics and a second to the Antarctic, and knows the routine of deep-sea oceanography as only a working scientist can. A New Yorker who attended Columbia and the University of Chicago, Engel won the George Polk Memorial Award in 1954 for science writing, and the American Heart Association's 1957 award for distinguished reporting in the field of heart and circulatory diseases. He has written a book on heart surgery, *The Operation*, as well as numerous magazine articles on a wide variety of scientific subjects.

Cover: WEST INDIAN BLUE TANGS DRIFT UNDER STAGHORN CORAL

Contents

TIME INC. BOOK DIVISION

Editor: NORMAN P. ROSS

Copy Director: WILLIAM JAY GOLD   *Art Director:* EDWARD A. HAMILTON

Chief of Research: BEATRICE T. DOBIE

EDITORIAL STAFF FOR "THE SEA":

Editor, LIFE Nature Library: MAITLAND EDEY

Assistants to the Editor: GEORGE McCUE, CARL SOLBERG

Designer: PAUL JENSEN

Chief Researcher: MARTHA TURNER

Researchers: DORIS BRY, RUTH GALAID,

ROXANNA SAYRE, MICHAEL SCHWARTZ

Picture Researchers: MARGARET K. GOLDSMITH, JOAN T. LYNCH

Art Associates: ALBERT J. DUNN, ROBERT L. YOUNG

Art Assistants: JAMES D. SMITH, MARK A. BINN

Copy Staff: MARIAN GORDON GOLDMAN,

SUZANNE SEIXAS, REBECCA CHAITIN, DOLORES A. LITTLES

•

Publisher: JEROME S. HARDY

General Manager: JOHN A. WATTERS

•

LIFE MAGAZINE

Editor	*Managing Editor*	*Publisher*
EDWARD K. THOMPSON	GEORGE P. HUNT	C. D. JACKSON

•

The text for the chapters of this book was written by Leonard Engel, the text for the picture essays by John Brick. Warren Young of LIFE Magazine was active in the early planning of the book. Others of the LIFE staff who helped are: Fritz Goro, staff photographer; Richard Pollard and the other members of the London Bureau; Ray Mackland, Picture Editor; George Caturani, Chief of the Foreign News Bureau; Thomas N. Carmichael, Chief of the Domestic News Bureau; Doris O'Neil, Chief of the LIFE Picture Library; and Content Peckham, Chief of the Time Inc. Bureau of Editorial Reference. Special assistance and advice were also provided by Nancy Genet, Alicia Hills and Patricia Hunt of LIFE.

Introduction

Despite their importance to mankind, the earth sciences have traditionally lagged behind the laboratory sciences. Perhaps the most backward subdivision of the earth sciences has been the obscure subject of oceanography, in which an attempt is made to advance our understanding of one particular part of our environment, namely the large fraction of our globe that is covered with salt water. The ocean is basic to all life. Therefore it is entirely fitting that this first volume in the LIFE Nature Library should be about the sea. This handsome book supplies a lively introduction to a fascinating subject.

Now that the public is becoming aware of the many things that are not yet well understood about the ocean and its contents, both the government and the universities have begun to respond. Our marine laboratories have been expanding very rapidly during the last 10 years. Able graduate students are being trained in all aspects of oceanography. New research ships are being built. Thus, we can expect rather rapid developments during the next 20 years. This new interest in oceanography is by no means confined to the United States. All the major maritime nations are taking part. Throughout the world roughly 50 research ships are constantly at sea. This means that about 600 technically trained people are at present actively working at sea, and that something like five times this number are studying the results of the field work in laboratories ashore.

What can we expect to emerge from this large increase in scientific effort? Clearly it will help to plug a big gap in our total knowledge concerning this earth on which we live and whose basic chemical and biological resources we must come to utilize more and more efficiently. However, we can expect considerably more than this. As oceanography has developed, it has become evident that there are many practical applications to basic oceanographic science. Through a thorough understanding of the ocean, followed by imaginative engineering, we can make our defenses much more secure than they now are, we can greatly improve marine transportation, we can exert some measure of control on climate and we can make available a vast food resource that automatically renews itself.

In its natural state, acre per acre, the sea is producing about as much as the land, yet man is only taking about one per cent of his present food requirements from the salt-water environment. When we come to farm the oceans we can expect them to produce much greater quantities of desirable food substances, just as farming on land has greatly increased the production of grains and vegetables and meat. Through proper management of the ocean, which will have to be by international agreement, we can greatly increase our well-being on the land.

COLUMBUS O'DONNELL ISELIN
Senior Physical Oceanographer
Woods Hole Oceanographic Institution

ATLANTIC ROLLERS move shoreward
during an autumnal sunset.
The breakers seen here, forming
off the beach at Gay Head,
on Martha's Vineyard, were born
during a storm in the open reaches
of the sea, at a point perhaps
hundreds of miles away from Gay Head.

1

The Matchless Phenomenon of the Sea

Our planet has the wrong name. Our ancestors named it Earth, after the soil they found all around them. So far as they thought about the planet as a whole, they believed for centuries that its surface consisted almost entirely of rocks and dirt, except for some smallish bodies of water like the Mediterranean Sea and the Black Sea. They knew about the Atlantic, of course, but they regarded it as a relatively narrow river running around the rim of the earth. If the ancients had known what the earth was really like, they undoubtedly would have named it Oceanus for the tremendous areas of water that cover 70.8 per cent of its surface.

Ours is indeed the watery planet; there is no other like it in the solar system. Mercury, the planet nearest the sun, has no free water at all. It is so small that it lacks sufficient gravity to hold an atmosphere or gases such as water vapor. Any such gases have long since escaped into space, if they ever existed, leaving the planet as dry and lifeless as the moon. (The moon too has no atmosphere, for the same reasons.)

Venus, the next closest planet to the sun, is large enough for its gravity to hold gases. It has an atmosphere, and a dense layer of white clouds which completely obscures its surface. However, these clouds are believed to consist of dry dust—only a trace of water vapor has ever been detected in Venus' atmosphere.

Farther out from the sun, Mars is believed to have a very thin atmosphere and also a small amount of surface water. Icy patches come and go on its poles like a thin frost at certain seasons of the Martian year. This tiny film of water is believed to support a sparse vegetation, but there is nothing on Mars resembling an ocean.

The giant planets that lie beyond Mars—Jupiter, Saturn, Uranus, Neptune—are all much too cold to have oceans, although they probably have a great deal of water in the form of ice. Ice makes up the outer layers of Jupiter and Saturn, and probably those of Uranus and Neptune as well. Saturn's rings are believed to consist of a swarm of ice particles, probably the remnants of an ice "moon" that approached the colossal planet too closely and was shattered by its gravitational pull. But none of Saturn's ice can become liquid. Even in areas that are warmed by the sun, surface temperatures on all of these outer planets range downward from 200 degrees below zero. As for the tiny outermost planet, Pluto, little is known about it, but it too is certainly far too cold to have a sea.

The earth's oceans are, then, unique in the sun's family of planets. Indeed it is remarkable that they exist at all. They do only because the earth has a surface temperature in the exceedingly narrow range within which water remains a liquid: in short, between 32 degrees Fahrenheit (below which, under ordinary conditions, it freezes) and 212 degrees Fahrenheit (above which it becomes a gas). In the vast reaches of the universe, temperatures tend to extremes—toward either the near-absolute-zero cold of interstellar space or the tens of millions of degrees found within stars. In-between temperatures, at which liquids can flow, are rare. Accordingly, nearly all of the matter in the universe is either flaming gas or frozen solid.

In a surprising variety of ways, the properties of water—liquid water—seem almost to have been designed expressly to make the world hospitable to life. Water has an unusually high capacity for storing heat, for example. As a result, the oceans act as great heat reservoirs, moderating the high temperatures of summer and the cold of winter. Unlike most liquids, which contract when they solidify, water expands by 9 per cent when it freezes. This means that ice floats instead of sinking. The ice is thus accessible to the sun's rays, which limit its spread, and the depths of cold polar seas remain unfrozen, enabling the creatures that live in them to survive.

Water can dissolve more substances than any other liquid known. No life could exist on earth for a moment if water did not have this capability. Living organisms, big and small, are chemical factories. They carry on the business of life by means of an amazing variety of chemical reactions, many of which occur only when water is present to dissolve the reacting substances

SEA MONSTER of Norwegian folklore, the Kraken, is shown sinking a ship. Said to be a mile and a half in girth, it had a circular flat shape and many arms. In 1752, a Norwegian bishop wrote that it darkened the water around it with an inky excretion, indicating that the sailors who reported it had seen a giant squid.

and bring their molecules together. Furthermore, water forms part of many of the chemical compounds found in living tissue. Seventy per cent of the human body is water. All forms of life need water—which must come ultimately from the oceans, even for the plants and animals that live on land.

Thus the sea, shaper of the world's surface, moderator of climate, cradle of life—unbelievably large. Convention divides it into four oceans: the Pacific (equal in size to the other three oceans combined), the Indian, the Atlantic and the Arctic. These, with their fringing gulfs and smaller seas, form an interconnected system through which an estimated 60,000,000,-000,000,000,000,000,000,000,000,000,000,000,000 water molecules circulate endlessly. This number is so huge as to simply overwhelm. There are so many molecules in a single glass of water that if they could somehow be tinted red for easy recognition, and then dumped in the sea, it would be impossible to scoop out another glass of water from anywhere in the sea without getting a good many of the same red molecules back. True, there would have to be a wait of many thousands of years for the original molecules to become thoroughly mixed into all oceans. But, once this happened, every glass of sea water in the world would contain the astonishing number of 1,500 red molecules. This tells more about how small water molecules are than about how big the ocean is. In fact, a water molecule is only one eighteen-billionth of an inch in diameter. Altogether, there are enough water molecules in the sea to fill a standpipe 75 miles in diameter and 70,000 miles high—which is approximately one third the distance from the earth to the moon.

In brief, the sea contains 330 million cubic miles of water. The volume of all land above sea level is only one eighteenth as great. Land's tallest peak, 29,028-foot-high Mount Everest, could be sunk without a trace in the ocean's greatest abyss, the 35,800-foot-deep Mariana Trench in the western Pacific. If all the irregularities on the earth's surface were to be smoothed out, both above and below the water, so that there were no dents or holes anywhere, no land would show at all. The ocean would cover the entire globe to a depth of 12,000 feet.

Locked up in all this water is a great variety of salts and minerals in solution. Oxygen, carbon dioxide and nitrogen from the atmosphere are also found dissolved in sea water. Dissolved oxygen is what marine creatures breathe. Dissolved carbon dioxide is used by green plants in the sea to produce food. So far as anyone knows, dissolved nitrogen has no function in the sea.

The average salinity of sea water is about 3.5 per cent; i.e., a cubic mile of sea water contains 166 million tons of salt, and the sea as a whole contains enough salt to cover the continents with a layer 500 feet thick. The salinity of the sea varies from place to place; this variation is a factor, as will be explained in another chapter, in causing ocean currents. But nowhere do the oceans approach the salinity of such inland seas as Great Salt Lake (average salt content, 28 per cent), the landlocked and concentrated remnant of an ancient sea that once covered much of western North America and left its salt behind.

Sea water is an important commercial source of common salt, magnesium metal, bromine and a number of other substances in wide industrial

ELEMENTS OF THE SEA

(per cubic mi. of water)

Oxygen	4,037,000,000 tons
Hydrogen	509,000,000 "
Chlorine	89,500,000 "
Sodium	49,500,000 "
Magnesium	6,125,000 "
Sulphur	4,240,000 "
Calcium	1,880,000 "
Potassium	1,790,000 "
Bromine	306,000 "
Carbon	132,000 "
Strontium	37,700 "
Boron	22,600 "
Silicon	14,130 "
Fluorine	6,125 "
Argon	2,825 "
Nitrogen	2,350 "
Lithium	940 "
Rubidium	565 "
Phosphorus	330 "
Iodine	235 "
Indium	94 "
Zinc	47 "
Iron	47 "
Aluminum	47 "
Molybdenum	47 "
Barium	29 "
Lead	14 "
Tin	14 "
Copper	14 "
Arsenic	14 "
Protactinium	14 "
Selenium	14 "
Vanadium	9.4 "
Manganese	9.4 "
Titanium	4.7 "
Thorium	3.3 "
Cesium	2.4 "
Antimony	2.4 "
Cobalt	2.3 "
Nickel	2.3 "
Cerium	1.8 "
Yttrium	1.4 "
Silver	1.4 "
Lanthanum	1.4 "
Krypton	1.4 "
Neon	1.4 "
Bismuth	1,885 lbs.
Tungsten	940 "
Xenon	940 "
Germanium	565 "
Cadmium	518 "
Chromium	470 "
Scandium	377 "
Mercury	280 "
Gallium	280 "
Tellurium	94 "
Niobium	47 "
Helium	47 "
Gold	38 "
Radium	.0003 "
Radon	.00000009 "

CHRISTOPHER COLUMBUS
(c. 1451-1506), a Genoese sailor
in Spanish employ, made four
voyages, discovering the
Bahamas, Cuba, Haiti,
Puerto Rico, Trinidad and other
West Indian islands. He reached
the mainland (Venezuela)
on his third voyage in 1498.

FERDINAND MAGELLAN
(c. 1480-1521), denied funds
by his native Portugal,
sailed under the Spanish flag
on his epochal voyage around the
world, which took three years.
Only 18 of his crew of about 280
survived. Magellan himself
was killed in the Philippines.

use. But many of the minerals found in the sea have no present commercial value. The difficulty is low concentration. For example, sea water contains gold at the rate of 38 pounds per cubic mile. This is the equivalent of a mere .0004 of an ounce—worth about a penny—per million gallons of water.

Where does all the salt in the sea come from? Part of it has come from the breaking up of rocks by frost and erosion, the gradual wearing away of mountains, which releases locked-in chemicals and permits them to be carried down to the ocean in solution by rain water. The rest has come from rocks beneath the ocean bed. There has been a constant slow addition to the sea's salinity over hundreds of millions of years. There is a curious way of deducing this: the body cells of animals (including fish) have a lower salt content than sea water has. From this it is possible to conclude that sea water, at the time life first took shape, was less salty than it is now.

The salts that have washed from the land into the ocean are only a tiny part of the total material that finds its way to the sea. The ocean is the earth's great "sink." Sooner or later it catches everything. Black mud that once grew corn and cotton in the Mississippi Valley, debris from the grinding down of a hundred mountain ranges, the cuttings of ten thousand river channels—all of these are on the ocean bottom. So are wind-blown dust, volcanic ash and even tiny meteorite globules from outer space.

Mixed in is the debris which the sea itself creates. When marine organisms die, their remains drift downward. A part of this unending "rain" never reaches the bottom, being consumed on the way down by deeper-dwelling organisms, or else lost to the powerful dissolving action of sea water itself. Over a long period of time, however, a great quantity of marine debris settles on the ocean floor.

Shells from diatoms and other microscopic creatures accumulate, along with other imperishable marine remains, forming an ever-thickening layer. In relatively shallow waters, where marine life is richest, and near the mouths of rivers which bring down debris from the land, the accumulations are many thousands of feet thick. Even in the deep ocean the beds of sediment are as much as 12,000 feet thick. Below them are other beds turned to rock by the forces of the earth and the passage of time.

What fascinates scientists is that the early history of the planet is locked in those deep-lying layers. The shells of extinct creatures are there, and maybe the imprints of even earlier soft-bodied creatures pressed into the mud—undisturbed eon after eon, crumbled by no wind, battered by no wave. The ooze at the bottom of the ocean is the quietest place in the world. By penetrating far into the sediments that lie there, scientists may learn some astonishing things about the earliest days of life on this planet.

Man is just now beginning to plumb the ocean's depths. Through most of his history he has been preoccupied only with its surface, as a source of food and as an avenue for travel. For much of recorded history he thought it was much smaller than it is. He did not, in fact, begin to apprehend its enormous size until the 14th and 15th Centuries. Ancient theories that the earth was a sphere were again coming to the fore, leading to Columbus' discovery of the Western Hemisphere in 1492, and culminating in Magellan's epochal feat of sailing around the world in 1519-1522. Even so, Mercator, the great map maker, believed as recently as 375 years ago that the earth was about equally divided between land and water, and that there was an immense land mass in the Southern Hemisphere to balance the masses of Europe, Asia and North America that lie in the Northern Hemisphere. Awareness of how watery the world really is came only with the voyages of the Dutch navigator Abel Tasman (for whom Tasmania is named) and England's illustrious explorer of the Pacific, Captain James Cook. Tasman and Cook proved that the southern seas were so huge and so empty that a luckless ship could conceivably sail around and around the world forever in southern latitudes without once sighting land.

But these discoveries and explorations dealt only with the surface of the sea. The depths have still barely been looked into. There has been more sounding and exploration of the ocean bottom in the last 20 years than in all the rest of history. For a long time there was no way of getting down to the bottom, or of learning what the depths were like without going down there. The deepest a free-swimming diver can go without underwater breathing gear is about 100 feet; this has been so for several thousand years. With the development of breathing apparatus, skin divers can now descend 200 feet or more, and helmeted divers can descend 600 feet if they breathe a special mixture of gases.

Modern submarines operate at depths of 600 feet. On January 23, 1960, the bathyscaph *Trieste*, a vessel designed for deep-water exploration, attained the ultimate in ocean depths when it spent 20 minutes on the bottom of the Challenger Deep in the Mariana Trench—nearly seven miles down. But most of man's present knowledge of the depths has not come from such record-breaking achievements. We have learned about the ocean bottom in the way we have been learning about space—by inventing instruments and techniques to bring back information from places to which a man cannot easily go.

Already some astonishing discoveries have been made. One of the most unexpected is that there are differences between the land and ocean areas that go down several hundred miles into the center of the earth. Oceanographers now know that the land and sea form distinct "provinces." The continents are made of granitic rock, whereas the bed of the deep ocean consists of a heavier kind of rock called basalt. Another piece of surprising new knowledge is that the earth's crust—the thin outermost layer—is far thinner under the sea than it is on land. Equally extraordinary was the recent discovery of a 40,000-mile submarine mountain range, by far the longest in the world, and now named the Mid-Ocean Ridge. This discovery has yet to appear in geography books. Nor do books on geography or minerals say anything about "nodules," mysterious potato-sized lumps of manganese, cobalt, iron and nickel existing in incredible profusion on certain parts of the ocean floor. Nodules are formed through the passage of time, by a process not fully understood, around bits of clay, sharks' teeth, or the ear bones of long-dead whales. Engineers are already busy designing vacuum cleaners with three-mile hoses to sweep up the millions of dollars that are lying there for the taking in nodule deposits.

But, given these geological mysteries, and many more that will undoubtedly follow, nothing quite equals in variety and interest the phenomenon of life in the sea. No one can make an accurate guess at the number of

GERARDUS MERCATOR (1512-1594), Flemish geographer, first called a book of maps an "atlas," and made cartography a science. His projection, still used, guides seamen by straight lines on flat charts instead of curved lines on globes.

JAMES COOK (1728-1779) in three South Pacific voyages explored New Zealand, Australia, Timor, Java, much of Polynesia and the Antarctic seas. After failing to find the fabled Northwest Passage on his last voyage, he was killed in Hawaii.

individual organisms that live there. We are far from having finished cataloguing the *kinds* of things that live there. New species are found by almost every expedition that sets out, occasionally an old species too. In 1938 a coelacanth, a kind of fish that was supposed to have become extinct 50 million years ago, suddenly turned up alive off the coast of South Africa. Almost anything can be expected from the sea—anything, that is, except sea monsters. Nobody believes any more in the kraken, a fabled creature of the depths that was said to be capable of swallowing an entire sailing vessel. And yet it may be presumptuous to rule out sea monsters entirely. A few years ago, a Danish research ship caught an eel larva which was so large that if it were in the same proportion to adult eels as larvae of other species are, it would reach 90 feet in length at maturity. So far, no giant eels have been caught, but another research vessel which went fishing for them did get hold of something 1,200 feet down that was large enough to bend a three-foot iron hook and escape.

Other large creatures lurk in the gathering darkness. Giant squid are found at 1,500 feet, and sperm whales dive that deep to eat them. There is something else, too, farther down at 3,000 feet, a sizable something that has been detected by explosive sonic methods, but nobody yet knows what it is or how big it is. So far, it is simply a squiggle on a piece of photographic paper. Still farther down, life gradually thins out. There is very little food at great depths and no sunlight whatsoever. As a result, the deeper one goes the smaller and sparser life becomes, although there are living things to be found at all levels right down to the deepest trench. Almost without exception, however, these creatures from another world are only a few inches long, and grotesquely specialized for their environment.

The life of the ocean is divided into distinct realms, each with its own group of creatures that feed upon each other and depend on each other in different ways. There is, first of all, the tidal zone, where land and sea meet. Then comes the realm of the shallow seas around the continents, which goes down to about 500 feet. It is in these two zones that the vast majority of all marine life occurs. The deep ocean adds two regions, the zone of light and the zone of perpetual darkness. In the clear waters of the western Pacific, light could still be seen at a depth of 1,000 feet through the portholes of the *Trieste* on its seven-mile dive. But for practical purposes the zone of light ends at about 600 feet. Below that level there is too little light to support the growth of the "grass" of the sea—the tiny, single-celled green plants whose ability to form sugar and starch with the aid of sunlight makes them the base of the great food pyramid of the ocean.

For purposes of classification and study, every form of animal life that lives on earth—or has lived—has been placed according to its structure in various basic groups called phyla. Some of the creatures in one phylum have traveled such evolutionarily different paths from others in the same phylum that it is hard to realize now that they are related. Octopuses, for example, belong to the same phylum as clams. Barnacles, which appear to be more closely related to clams, are actually cousins of lobsters. It is a remarkable fact that certain phyla seem to inhabit every region of the sea.

What may be even more remarkable is that every phylum on land is also represented in the ocean. We have, in truth, come from the sea.

Animal Phyla of the Sea

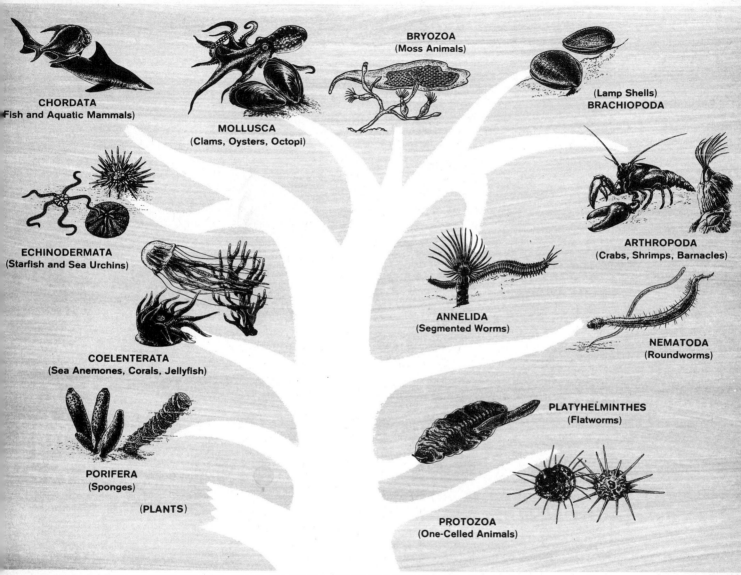

BRYOZOA
(Moss Animals)

CHORDATA
(Fish and Aquatic Mammals)

MOLLUSCA
(Clams, Oysters, Octopi)

(Lamp Shells)
BRACHIOPODA

ECHINODERMATA
(Starfish and Sea Urchins)

ARTHROPODA
(Crabs, Shrimps, Barnacles)

ANNELIDA
(Segmented Worms)

NEMATODA
(Roundworms)

COELENTERATA
(Sea Anemones, Corals, Jellyfish)

PLATYHELMINTHES
(Flatworms)

PORIFERA
(Sponges)

(PLANTS)

PROTOZOA
(One-Celled Animals)

THE SEA, WHERE LIFE FIRST EVOLVED, HOLDS ALL MAJOR ANIMAL GROUPINGS, FROM SIMPLE PROTOZOA TO COMPLEX MAMMALS

All animal life may be divided into 22 major groups, or phyla, all of which occur in the sea and all of which probably first evolved there. The 12 most important marine phyla are shown above. Whether elementary types like protozoa, or elaborate creatures like fish or lobsters, all are descended from long-lost early forms.

15

Segmented Worms

Ten of the 22 animal phyla are worms. In the sea the most important worm phylum consists of the annelids, whose body plan is a hollow tube divided into small compartments. Many thousands of kinds of annelids live in every part of the ocean, from the beach to the abyss.

PUGNACIOUS WORMS, two four-inch annelids, duel with horny pincers which can inflict a painful nip on a human hand. The interior partitioning is shown by the rings around the body, and the word "annelid" comes from the Latin *anellus*, meaning "ring." A West Coast relative of the European animals above grows to be three feet long.

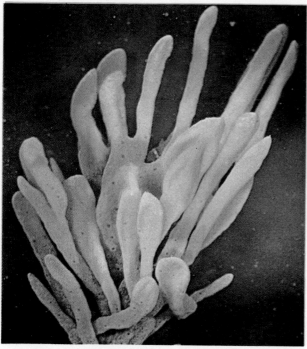

DEAD MEN'S FINGERS is an East Coast sponge, often seen when its bleached skeleton washes ashore. Small surface holes give the phylum the name Porifera (pore bearers).

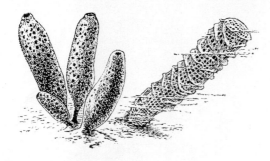

Phylum Porifera

Sponges

A hundred years ago, biologists thought the sponge was a plant. It sits quietly, it does not respond when you touch it, and it has no tentacles or claws for catching food. But closer study has shown the lumpish sponge to be an active animal. Its body is dotted with small holes connected to a few larger ones through interior canals. Whiplike appendages in these passages beat furiously, pumping water in through the small openings and out through the large. Food morsels are filtered out and eaten; a sponge must filter out a ton of water before it can gain an ounce in its body weight.

FRINGED BASKET is a Jamaican sponge with an eight-inch central opening. Many small animals live in large sponges; 17,000 were collected from a single giant Florida specimen.

AZURE VASE (*below*) is a 10-inch-high Bahamian sponge. The household sponge is the dried and treated skeleton of a few species found in the Mediterranean and off Florida.

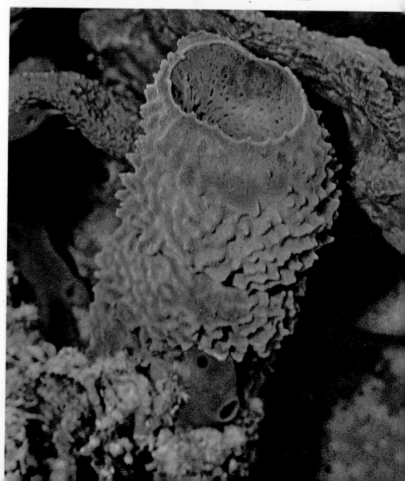

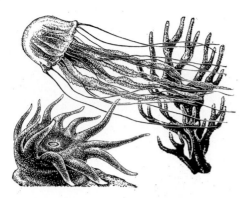

Phylum Coelenterata

Sea Anemones, Corals and Jellyfish

Few phyla take more shapes than the coelenterates. Gossamer jellyfish pulsate through the open sea. The corals hide in their stony shelters. Flowerlike sea anemones wave in underwater gardens. But the many shapes of the coelenterates are built around a single body plan: a hollow pouch with a circlet of tentacles around a mouth. This central cavity, in which the animal's food is digested, is called a "coelenteron," Greek for "hollow gut."

A HUNGRY CORAL engulfs a food morsel. Many soft-bodied coral animals together build the limestone apartment houses we know as coral reefs.

A DECEPTIVE ANEMONE (*opposite*) looks like a harmless flower but is actually a vicious carnivore. Poison darts that can stun a fish stud its tentacles.

A DRIFTING JELLYFISH (*right*) has the same basic design as a sea anemone—only upside down. The pink spots around the tentacles are primitive eyes.

AN ANEMONE SHRIMP (*above*), a South Sea native, has a rare form of camouflage. It is transparent except for the few disconnected spots marking the locations of vital organs.

A BARRIER REEF CRAB (*below*), is only an inch wide. It scuttles along Australian beaches by night, eating dead plants and animals. Stalked eyes are found in all the crabs.

Phylum Arthropoda

Crabs, Shrimps and Barnacles

Three fourths of all animal species are arthropods. Over 25,000 kinds live in the sea and 600,000, mostly insects, live on land. All arthropods have an outer shell which they shed as they grow, and all have jointed limbs. The word "arthropod" means "jointed leg."

A DROMID CRAB (*below*), inhabitant of a Bermuda reef, conceals its bright color by holding a shell overhead with two legs. It often uses a live sponge for the same purpose.

GOOSENECK BARNACLES are arthropods that hang upside down on tough stalks and kick food into their mouths with feathery feet. A shell protects their bodies.

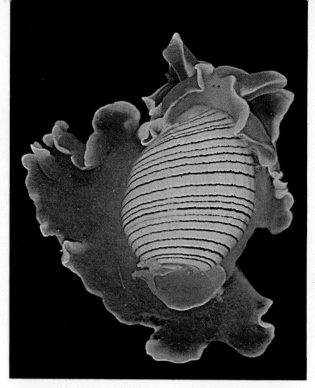

ROSE-PETAL BUBBLE SHELL is a snail found in the Great Barrier Reef. The flowing blue film is called the mantle, and is the organ in the mollusks which secretes the shell.

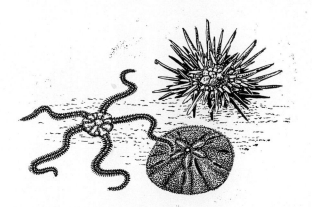

Phylum Echinodermata

Starfish and Sea Urchins

The starfish with its many arms has no right or left, only top and bottom. This spokelike design is characteristic of the phylum. Stiffening the echinoderm is a skeleton formed of spiny plates that stick through the skin and account for the name "echinoderm" (hedgehog skin).

Phylum Mollusca

Clams, Oysters and Octopuses

Mollusca means "soft-bodied," and inside its hard shell the average mollusk is a tender and often tasty animal. Mollusks have a muscular foot, and many of them use it to move at an extremely slow pace. But in the octopuses, the foot is divided into eight tentacles.

UNDERWATER CATERPILLAR, the clown sea slug (*opposite*) is a Pacific Coast mollusk that has no shell. Experts believe a disagreeable taste protects it from its enemies.

PURPLE SUN-STAR lives on the Atlantic Coast. On its underside are a mouth and dozens of suction-cup feet. There are 2,000 kinds of starfish, some growing three feet across.

23

Sea Colander
Phyllaria dermatodea

Sea Grapes

Dog Whelks   Periwinkles

Edible Mussels

Sea Vases

Purple Starfish

Pink Hearted Hydroids

Sea Anemone

Coralline Algae

Redbeard Sponge   Oyster Drills

Blood Starfish

Mussel Shell   Ribbed Mussels   Rock Barnacles

Sea Pork

Sand Dollar and Shell

Sun Star

24   Irish Moss

Mud Star

Common Starfish

Moon Snail Shell

Brittle Star

Razor Clam Shell

Boat Shell

Phylum Chordata

Fish and Aquatic Mammals

The chordates rule the sea. They differ from all other creatures by having an internal body support. In primitive forms, this may be little more than a tough rod wrapped in elastic tissue. More often, as in fish, it has been replaced by a chain of bony links called vertebrae, to which powerful muscles can be attached. Thus is derived the strength, controlled by a complex nervous system, that makes the chordates masters of the sea.

The painting below shows a 4,000-foot-deep cross section of the open sea, the heart of the marine chordate's domain. Familiar food fish and sport fish race in its top waters and burst exuberantly through the surface. Here too swim the sharks, the 3,000-pound manta and an ungainly sunfish that dwarfs a man. In mid-depths the whale, the largest chordate, battles the giant squid, the largest animal without a backbone.

Deeper down in twilight, then in darkness, live forms so obscure, they are known only by scientific names. Many are hideous flesh eaters, and one tiny monster, the *Chiasmodon*, can swallow fish bigger than itself. In the blackness, only patterns of luminous dots distinguish friend from foe.

1 Manta 20 ft.
2 Blue marlin 10 ft.
3 Sailfish 8 ft.
4 Flying fish 9 in.
5 Sunfish 7 ft.
6 Oceanic bonito 2 ft.
7 Dolphin 4 ft.
8 Pilot fish 9 in.
9 White-tipped shark 7 ft.
10 Bluefin tuna 7 ft.
11 Giant squid 55 ft.
12 Sperm whale 60 ft.
13 *Sternoptyx diaphana* 2 in.
14 *Diretmus argenteus* 2 in.
15 Eel larva 4 in.
16 Hatchet fish 1 in.
17 *Lamprotoxus flagellibarba* 8 in.
18 *Platyberix opalescens* 3 in.
19 Roosterfish 15 ft.
20 Viperfish 12 in.
21 Prawn 4 in.
22 *Photostomias guernei* 7 in.
23 Lantern fish 3 in.
24 *Chiasmodon niger* 2 in.
25 *Opisthoproctus soleatus* 1 in.
26 *Melanocetus johnsoni* 2 in.
27 Snipe eel 2 ft.

FOLD OUT: DO NOT TEAR

A GAUDY WRASSE (*opposite*) wheels over a Pacific reef, using its fins as rudders. Color varies with the age and sex of the fish. The strong blue teeth are used to open shellfish.

TWO FLYING FISH skim over California waters. One is airborne, the other sculls with its tail to gain speed. Flying fish do not actually fly but make glides up to 50 yards.

The Blueprint of a Swimmer

Water is almost 800 times denser than air. As any swimmer or ship designer will testify, it relentlessly holds back anything that tries to speed through it. But the fish has been engineered to beat the ocean's drag. Speedsters like the blue marlin hit 50 miles an hour and dolphins have been clocked at 37 miles per hour.

The fish body is a slippery, water-cutting form that is usually lens-shaped like the wrasse's, or long and narrow like the flying fish's. Inside there is often a bladder filled with gas. This swim bladder enables a fish to hover at its characteristic level with minimum effort. To swim, the fish points its head where it wants to go and wriggles the rest of its body. Fins are used for balance, for steering and as brakes.

Not much is known about how fish sleep. The wrasse lies on its side on the bottom under a cover of sand. A wrasse relative, the parrot fish, secretes a blanket of disagreeable slime about itself and naps in safety. Many fish never seem to sleep at all. The flying fish may be one of these insomniacs. On many a black night it can be found sailing 20 feet above the water.

FOUR MANTA RAYS, FRIGHTENED BY SOME UNDERWATER ENEMY, JUMP HIGH OUT OF THE PACIFIC OFF THE MEXICAN COAST NEAR

The Devilfish, Huge but Harmless

In spite of its name and appearance, the manta ray, or devilfish, is a gentle creature that flaps through the water, eating nothing larger than a shrimp. Yet it comes from a family of undesirables, including the shark and the barbtailed sting ray. The sharks and rays are among the original fish in the sea. Their supple bodies are reinforced with cartilage skeletons, and their blood is as bitter as the sea water itself. The other fish, with their brittle bones, probably evolved in fresh water and returned to the sea. Their blood is much less salty than the ocean's brine.

READY TO LAND (*right*), the manta ray levels off before making a belly-whopping re-entry. Mantas may also jump from the water to dislodge bothersome parasites.

A NETTED MANTA (*left*) is hoisted onto a fishing vessel's deck. The head flaps located just over the gill slits are believed to funnel food into the animal's mouth.

32

ACAPULCO. THESE IMMENSE RAYS GROW 20 FEET ACROSS, WEIGH OVER A TON AND A HALF. THEY CAN LEAP 15 FEET OUT OF WATER

THE TOADFISH is a belligerent bottom dweller along the American East Coast. It has four poisonous spines on its back and gill covers that cause painful but not fatal wounds.

Small but Dangerous

The poisonous land animals have their counterparts in the sea. Dozens of fish, including the ones pictured here, have hollow spines on their bodies which can inject venom into an enemy. Humans touching these fish often receive stings that result in excruciating pain, severe shock and even death. Still another large group of fish is poisonous when eaten. The toxins in the fish's flesh usually come from a microscopic plant on which it feeds. This toxicity is especially dangerous since a variety of fish may be safe to eat one day but deadly the next. Fatalities run to only 7 per cent, but recovery from this type of poisoning may take years.

THE DEADLY STONEFISH (*below*) has a venom that can kill a man in a few hours. Waders often step on it as it lies in the shallow reef waters of the Indian and Pacific Oceans.

THE ZEBRA FISH is also called the turkeyfish because it swims languidly through the warm waters of the Indian and Pacific Oceans, spreading its long fins like the feathers

of a strutting gobbler. But, hidden among the lacy frills, the zebra fish has 18 needle-like poison spines. Possibly because of its armament, this creature is quite fearless, and many skin divers are stung when they reach out to touch it as it swims slowly by. Zebra-fish venom causes severe pain and sometimes results in paralysis and even death.

2

The
Origin of
the Sea

The sea is old, old almost beyond imagining. And the earth itself is still older. To give some idea of just how old, we might try setting the ages of geologic time against the span of our own 12-month year. By that comparison, if we say the earth was first formed in January and its crust was finally formed about February, then the primeval ocean came into being perhaps as early as March, certainly no later than June. By the same yardstick, we would say that the first life appeared in August and the earliest fossils in November, dinosaurs had their day about mid-December and the age of man did not begin until the last day of the last week of the year—in fact, his real ascent from the animals did not start until about 10:30 p.m. on the 365th day.

This immense journey through geologic time began some four to six billion years ago. That, most astronomers believe, is about when the earth was born. In the view now most widely favored among scientists, the sun and its planets, including the earth, were all formed at the same time out of the same cloud of dust and gas. According to this gas-cloud hypothesis, our solar system began as one of the great whirling clouds of gas that drifted through the universe. Over a period of perhaps many millions of years, particles and gas molecules in this cloud were pulled to its center by gravitational forces. Here they piled up as a growing ball of gas and dust—the sun. But besides this single nucleus, a number of smaller satellite nuclei also developed in the cloud that gave birth to the sun. These contracted, too, but were too small to generate the temperatures required to light stellar fires. They became planets, orbiting around the central star, instead of stars themselves. So the earth came into existence.

Whether the earth ever grew hot enough to become a molten ball is a point on which scientists now are in lively disagreement. But, however it may have started out, virtually all experts agree that it did swiftly heat up, from the collision of atoms squeezed together by gravity and from radioactivity deep inside the "protoearth." Most geologists still think that at one point the earth's surface was much hotter than it is now.

There was yet no sea. The primeval ocean was created when the temperature of the earth's surface fell below the boiling point of water. Water was present on earth from the beginning, but pent-up in the interior rock, and was released by processes occurring in the infant earth. Water vapor rose in great cloud masses that enveloped and darkened the earth. For a time the new planet's surface may have been so hot that no moisture could fall without immediately being converted to steam. Yet even this "rain" helped carry away heat from the hot rocks, and sped the cooling of the planet by transferring heat from the earth to the upper layers of the atmosphere, where it could be dissipated into space.

For perhaps thousands of years the great overhanging cloud masses prevented the sun's rays from reaching the face of the earth. It took that long for the crust to cool from the freezing point of rocks (1,000 to 2,000 degrees Fahrenheit) to the boiling point of water (212 degrees Fahrenheit). Finally the day came when the falling raindrops did not hiss away in steam, but stayed to start filling the crevices and corners of the naked planet. Then it rained, and the accumulation of the seas began. The accumulation did not take place (in the opinion of modern geologists) through "the greatest deluge of all time" that has so often been described. So far as anyone can tell, it may merely have rained as it rains today. Nature has plenty of time. It probably took a billion years to fill the oceans. William Rubey, of the United States Geological Survey, thinks that the low valleys and shallow depressions that formed the early seas contained only 5 to 10 per cent of the volume of water in the sea today. But as the eons have passed, water vapor has kept coming up through volcanoes and fumaroles, adding to the moisture of the atmosphere and thus to the bulk of the seas.

All this may help explain how the ocean got its water, but it does not shed much light on the origins of the ocean basins themselves. There have been some ingenious explanations. In 1878, Sir George Darwin—the son of Charles Darwin—suggested that when the earth's crust was still partly liquid, a great chunk may have been ripped out of the earth's body where the Pacific Ocean now is, and flung into orbit as the moon. Later calculations showed that this could not have happened. If the Pacific basin was created during an almost molten period in the earth's crust, as Darwin suggested, it would be older than the Atlantic basin. But that may not be so. Bruce C. Heezen of the Lamont Geological Observatory, one of the world's foremost experts on ocean-bottom topography, is authority for the statement that no physical evidence has yet been found that one ocean basin is older than another.

Of course, though scientists know comparatively little of geological events that took place more than 500 or 600 million years ago, they feel quite sure that the frontiers of the sea kept changing with the slow drip of the ages. They recognize that there have been marked movements in the earth's crust. Whole mountain systems have been raised by these crustal movements and by volcanoes, then ground down again by erosion, their crumbling bits swept into the sea. Low-lying regions of the land have been invaded many times as sea levels changed in response to movements of the earth's crust. The "roof of the world"—the Himalayas—was once under water. And yet it is believed that something roughly like the present continental masses has always existed, and that the deep ocean basins have always lain between them. Their sizes and shapes may have varied, but some parts of today's continents must have always existed. The reason for this belief is the discovery, mentioned in Chapter 1, that deep rock layers under the sea are fundamentally different from those under the land.

Some say life appeared on earth two billion years ago or possibly even earlier. Some put the time a little nearer the present. There is no clear-cut evidence from which the date can be determined. The assumption of modern science is that the first "living" things must have been molecules possessing the property that above all distinguishes the living from the nonliving, the ability to reproduce themselves. They must have first taken shape in the environment of the sea, because water was indispensable to their formation. Moreover, life stepped forth from the sea only relatively late in geological times. And small though they would be by the scale of all the living creatures we know, they must have been very large molecules. We may even venture to imagine some of the circumstances that attended their formation: a blanket of cloud that helped keep the earth warm, an atmosphere stinking of methane (marsh gas) and ammonia, an oceanic vat of dissolving minerals in which giant molecule compounds of carbon combined and recombined until the right combination was finally reached.

Whatever the complex chemistry of life that may have been set in motion, it eventually led to the evolution of simple, single-celled organisms. To subsist, these first living creatures of the sea had to consume smaller molecules of the proper kind. Then a second event undoubtedly happened, almost as important as the leap into life itself. Certain living organisms acquired the ability to capture energy from sunlight and use it to make food out of the chemicals dissolved in the sea. Such living things took the carbon dioxide dissolved in sea water and, by using sunlight, were able to produce sugar, at the same time releasing oxygen. This did not happen all at once, but over a long period and in several stages. The organisms involved in this process were plants. Other organisms, unable

GEOLOGIC TIME SCALE

PLEISTOCENE
0-1 million years ago.
Four ice ages. Many mammals become extinct. Man appears.

TERTIARY
1-63 million years ago.
Continent building. Modern plants, dominance of mammals.

CRETACEOUS
63-135 million years ago.
Water inundates much of earth. Dinosaurs become extinct.

JURASSIC
135-181 million years ago.
Mild climates. Giant land and sea dinosaurs, toothed birds.

TRIASSIC
181-230 million years ago.
Arid climate. Dinosaurs, mammal prototypes, first pupal insects.

PERMIAN
230-280 million years ago.
Extremes of climate. Trilobites become extinct. Reptiles flourish.

CARBONIFEROUS
280-345 million years ago.
Warm and humid. Coal swamp forests, gigantic insects.

DEVONIAN
345-405 million years ago.
Varied climate. Many fish. Amphibians, insects evolve.

SILURIAN
405-425 million years ago.
Mild climate. Many coral reefs. First life on land.

ORDOVICIAN
425-500 million years ago.
Mild climate. Seaweeds, clams, nautiloids, first vertebrates.

CAMBRIAN
500-600 million years ago.
Moderate upheavals. Trilobites, mollusks, first crustaceans.

PRE-CAMBRIAN
600-? million years ago.
Constant earth upheavals. Soft-bodied marine animals.

to perform this miracle (called photosynthesis) but still needing organic food, found they could live on plants. These were animals.

We think of photosynthesis as merely a food-producing process. Actually, the production of free oxygen as a by-product is just as important. The oxygen in the air which we breathe today was not here before green plants began to manufacture it. Nor was there any in the ancient seas before then. Plants supply us—and marine animals, too—not only with food, but with oxygen to breathe. Without oxygen as well as plant food, no animal could exist.

From the day life first awoke in the waters, the sea has been a cradle endlessly rocking. The first organisms of which there is any definite trace are the blue-green algae, whose fossil remains have been found in Canada and appear to be at least a billion years old. Yet, after the leap that captured sunlight, plants never evolved very far in the sea. Today there are only 30 species of "higher" plants in ocean waters—compared with some 175,000 flowering plants on land. Most marine plants are primitive and cannot be very different from ancient forms. The great development of plants took place after they led the way ashore, some 400 million years ago.

Animals, on the other hand, thrived in the water and began to display the most extraordinary diversity almost as soon as the jump was made from single-celled to many-celled forms. A few, such as the lowly sponges, have remained little more than permanent colonies; each cell of a sponge feeds itself by stirring the water with a tiny, whiplike whisker to draw in microorganisms close enough to ingest them in the primitive style of single-celled animals. But other multicellular animals evolved mouths, stomachs, body cavities, nervous systems, coordinated means of locomotion—the typical features by which animals are distinguished.

The record of fossils imprinted in rock is our source for the early history of living things. Until a few years ago, such records began with what scientists called the Cambrian period, whose rocks were formed 600 to 500 million years ago. During that period animals first appeared with the hard shells that make good fossils. The things that preceded them were so soft-bodied that they left few traces of themselves. Recently, however, many impressions left in mud and sand by Pre-Cambrian animals have been found in England and South Australia. They show the existence, some 700 million or more years ago, of jellyfish (the most primitive creatures to possess mouth and stomach); segmented worms and creatures like flatworms (among the first organisms with nervous system and brain); soft corals; and two creatures completely unlike any other known animal, living or extinct—one a tiny, kite-shaped organism, the other a round, fringed creature with three arms curving out from a central hub. How long these shadowy creatures had been in existence, or what they sprang from, is unknown. All we know is that they did exist, from the faint impressions which their bodies left in the mud when they died.

From Cambrian times a wealth of fossils fills out the rock pages of evolutionary history, although no animal had yet appeared with a backbone and no plant or animal had evolved that was capable of venturing on the forbidden land. The sea, especially the sunlit shallows, remained the nursery

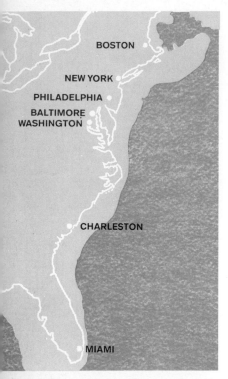

CHANGES IN SEA LEVEL, due to ice ages, are shown in two maps of U.S. East Coast. Extreme glaciation will drop the sea level 300 feet, leaving many seaports high and dry (*top*). If all the polar ice melts, the seas may rise as much as 300 feet, covering Florida and other coastal areas (*bottom*).

of life. There, animals with protective shells, plates and skins multiplied. Lamp shells, snails, graptolites (drifting, hydralike creatures with fantastic branching skeletons) appeared. But the dominant forms were arthropods, the phylum to which crabs and lobsters, spiders and insects belong. The chief of the arthropods of the Cambrian sea floor was a many-legged creature called the trilobite. This creeping scavenger was the giant of its day, achieving lengths of three inches and occasionally as much as 18 inches. Trilobites outnumbered all other preserved Cambrian animals put together, and survived on earth for the impressive span of 370 million years.

In the Ordovician age which followed (500 to 425 million years ago), mollusks called nautiloids, trailing shells up to 16 feet long, took over the ocean floor. Clams, starfish and corals put in their appearance. It was not until the Silurian age (425 to 405 million years ago) that fish—the first animals with backbones—arrived on the scene in abundance. The other great event of the Silurian period was the invasion of the land by the higher plants, when a great epoch of mountain-building drove the sea back from low-lying land areas. Soon afterward the first animal, a small sea scorpion, crawled up the beach and stayed.

By the next era, the Devonian (405-345 million years ago), the sea had much the look of today. Fish had diversified into forms easily recognizable as kin to modern fish. Their vastly increased mobility, strength and intelligence had made them the dominant form of marine life. A few of them followed the scorpion ashore and developed into the first land-dwelling vertebrates. Man is descended from one such land-invading fish.

On the whole, the earth that witnessed these slow changes was a quiet place, and the climate remained agreeably warm for enormously long periods. But from their studies of rocks, scientists know that occasional interludes of violence overtook the earth. One such time of crisis was the Permian age, about 250 million years ago, when volcanoes exploded, the Appalachian Mountains reared in North America, and glaciers are thought to have spread across equatorial Africa, South America and India. Another critical time began in the dawn of our own geologic age a million years ago, when the first of four successive ice invasions rolled across the planet.

Why did the ice invasions, hitherto rare, suddenly spread all over the world? This is a question that scientists have been asking ever since the Swiss naturalist Louis Agassiz, poking among the glaciers of his native Alps, proved a century and a quarter ago that there actually were ice ages. Variations in the sun's output of energy, changes of the earth's position in relation to the sun, and outpourings of volcanic dust into the earth's atmosphere have all been blamed for the snow that fell till the continents were buried. It remained for some sharp-eyed scientists punching holes in the ocean floor to come up with the latest theory.

Since the early 1930s, when a scientist at the Woods Hole Oceanographic Institution in Massachusetts dropped a long, heavily weighted tube into beds of sea-floor sediment, oceanographers have tested many devices for probing the sedimentary layers of mud and dead marine organisms on the ocean bottom. The most efficient to date, the piston corer—a device that drives a steel tube with a sharp cutting edge deep into the ocean floor —brings back long cylinders of sediment, known as cores, of up to 65 feet in length. These are stratified like a multilayer cake, the different strata representing hundreds of thousands of years of undisturbed history, and occasionally even older bits of the past. A few years ago, research vessels brought up scores of bottom cores from the Atlantic and the Gulf of Mexico which indicated that there may have been a sudden warming of the Atlantic 10,000 to 15,000 years ago. Layers of marine organisms previously abundant in the Atlantic were suddenly covered by a layer of others known to require higher temperatures. The demarcation line between the two types of fossils in some cores was as sharp as a pencil line.

What caused this? Two oceanographers of the Lamont Geological Observatory, Maurice Ewing and William L. Donn, wondered mightily about it. What was particularly puzzling to them was that the abrupt warming of the Atlantic had come at a time when the climate was still very cold. True, the advance of the ice had stopped. But the ice was still there, huge masses of it, from the North Pole all the way down to Wisconsin.

In casting about for an explanation, Ewing and Donn considered a radical possibility: suppose the surface of the Arctic had once been open. It would have poured great quantities of cold water into the Atlantic, thus causing the Atlantic to cool. Then suppose that the Arctic had subsequently frozen over. This would have reduced the outpouring of cold water and allowed the Atlantic to get warmer.

It was clear to the two Lamont scientists that an open Arctic Ocean, free of ice, would have profound effects on climate. They prepared weather maps to see what these effects might be. The maps showed that an open Arctic, fed by warm Atlantic currents and whipped by polar winds, would put immense volumes of water vapor into the polar atmosphere. This in turn would lead to great blizzards over the nearby shores of North America, Europe and Siberia, and to the formation, over thousands of years, of continent-blanketing ice sheets.

The accumulation of ice on the land, however, would take water from the sea and lower the level of the ocean. Sooner or later, the drop in sea level would greatly reduce the flow of warm water into the Arctic, because the main channel between the Atlantic and the Arctic—the 1,100-mile gap between Greenland and Norway—is relatively shallow. At that point, the Arctic would freeze. This would cut off the flow of water vapor to the polar atmosphere, and finally put an end to the ice-age blizzards. So Ewing and Donn, who started out to find why the Atlantic had suddenly become warmer thousands of years ago, wound up with a new theory of the ice ages. To summarize it: open Arctic makes blizzards that make ice sheets; freezing of Arctic halts blizzards and ends the march of the ice.

The Ewing-Donn hypothesis is by no means accepted by all geologists. But interesting evidence from the field of anthropology has been found that the Arctic was in fact open during the ice ages. Anthropologists have found flints and other signs of human habitation more than 10,000 years old on "permanently" frozen shores of the Arctic in northern Canada. The first of these finds was made several decades ago and has been a great puzzle to anthropologists, because man does not live on a permanently frozen shore where he can obtain no food. Now it is quite clear: the Arctic was open when those men lived there.

The Ewing-Donn hypothesis raises two questions. The first: what started the round of ice ages? This is an extremely taxing question. The best theory has to do with another astonishing aspect of the earth which most of us are unaware of. And that is that the Poles were not always where they are now. It is well established today that they have wandered over the earth since the planet came into being. Nobody knows just how or why this happens, but there is plenty of evidence that it does happen. Anyone who has ever sailed a boat or used a compass knows that the compass needle always points to a spot called the Magnetic Pole, which is located in Canada not too far from the true Pole. Now, some rocks have iron particles in them, and these particles will tend to "point" toward a Pole when the rocks are being formed, just as a compass needle does, or as iron filings do in a magnetic field. If we could find a number of rocks whose iron particles were pointing toward the Hawaiian Islands, let us say, it might not be unreasonable to assume that when the rock was formed eons ago and these particles were "frozen" into place, a Magnetic Pole may have been in the vicinity of Hawaii. One proof that Magnetic Poles have shifted lies in the fact that rocks have been found with iron particles pointing in many directions, suggesting that the Poles have had many locations in times past.

One may wonder what that has to do with the start of ice ages. It is simply this: Poles tend to be cold because the sun's rays hit them at a slant and, as a result, pour less concentrated heat on them. Also, the greater the slant, the greater the distance through the atmosphere the rays will have to travel, and the greater the heat loss. Therefore, if it is cold enough to snow anywhere on earth, it will snow at the Poles. If the North Pole is located in the Pacific near Hawaii, say, the snow will fall into the ocean and there will be no build-up of icecaps or glaciers—in short, no ice age. Thus, for ice ages to take place, the Poles must be located in certain places on earth favorable for an accumulation of snow.

The second question that the Ewing-Donn theory raises is: aren't we in for more ice ages? Yes, say Ewing and Donn, as long as the Poles remain where they are. We are in an interglacial stage at the moment. The ice sheet is no longer probing down to Wisconsin, as it was 11,000 years ago. It may well recede farther if the Arctic Ocean remains frozen, though short-term trends are misleading. A thousand years ago, southern Greenland was warm enough for large colonies of Norsemen to live there. But 200 years ago saw the onset of what may have been the coldest century since before the time of Christ. It began to get warm again about 1880 and continued warming until 1940. Now, glaciers seem to be growing again. These, however, are short-range changes. We can only say that we do not yet know enough about ice ages to predict when the next one will come. All we can be sure of is that it will not be here for hundreds of years, most probably not for thousands.

So, if the Poles will stay put, man can look for the kind of weather he has now, and some day much colder weather. Forever is a risky word, but there is nothing on the horizon, either in theory or in observation, to suggest that there will be a return to the fantastically long periods when the creatures of the past lived and died in a world whose tropical climate seemed never to change at all.

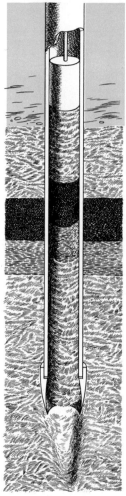

PISTON CORER, which can pick up a sediment sample 65 feet long, consists of a metal tube and an internal piston. When the rig hits bottom, the piston stops, but the tube goes on into the mud, enclosing a sample which is held by clasps at the tip of the tube.

NINETY MILLION YEARS AGO A 14-FOOT FISH, THE PORTHEUS, ATTACKED AND SWALLOWED A SIX-FOOT FISH WHOLE. THE PORTHEUS

SITE OF THE FIND was a rock slab in Kansas that was once under a shallow sea covering most areas of the American Midwest. The bulldog-visaged Portheus and its six-foot prey, the Ichthyodectes, are remote ancestors of herring.

44

DIED ALMOST IMMEDIATELY AFTER THE HEAVY MEAL, TO BE TRANSFORMED FINALLY INTO A VIVID FOSSIL RECORD OF FATAL GLUTTONY

The Story in Stone

In sedimentary rock layers that were formed on the floors of vanished oceans are found skeletons, shells and other fossil traces of the life that formerly lived in those seas. The combined evidence of fossils and of rock strata in which they were found enables scientists to re-create ancient seascapes, like those reproduced on the following pages. A fossil such as the one above, capturing a vital moment in the life of an animal that has long since disappeared from the earth, is an extraordinary rarity.

FOSSIL SEA LILIES, animals with flowerlike bodies (*above*), are 340 million years old. They were believed extinct until living specimens were discovered in 1873.

GIANT TRILOBITE, Isotelus (*below*), one of thousands of known species, was 18 inches long. Trilobites ruled the earth for 100 million years, are now all extinct.

The fossil record forms a basis for paintings which bring
the ancient oceans back to life. Simple creatures
representing nearly all phyla swarmed through the early seas

Life in the Cambrian Age

The painting above shows how life must have looked in a vanished ocean that covered central Europe during the Cambrian age, 600 million years ago. Like the pictures that follow, it is an accurate reconstruction, from fossil remains, made by a collaboration of scientist and artist.

The Cambrian sea teemed with life. All phyla of animals known today except perhaps the chordates lived in its waters. Among these the dominant form was a primitive arthropod, the trilobite, shown creeping in the foreground

and at right. Called trilobites because their protective coating was divided lengthwise into three parts, these prolific animals were sea-floor scavengers resembling crabs. Most were less than four inches long, although the giant trilobite (*foreground*) reached a length of 18 inches. Primitive sponges were also common, like the vase-shaped forms with glassy skeletons shown bobbing at left and right. Hovering in front of a cluster of waving algae is a group of jellyfish which have left traces in ancient rocks and sediments.

Cone-Crowned Monsters Ruled the Sea 400 Million Years Ago

By the Silurian age, some 75 million years later, the trilobites (*foreground, left*) had clearly lost their primacy to new cone-shaped monsters called nautiloids. These bizarre creatures, whose leering eyes, beetling brows and party-hat shells are reminiscent of Punch, attained lengths

of 16 feet. Like the chambered nautilus, the only surviving relic of their kind, these animals occupied only the forepart of their shells: the rest was partitioned in chambers filled with gas that helped buoy the tenant as it prowled for prey on spidery tentacles. Other ancient forms teemed around these giant carnivores. Primitive snails in coiled shells plowed the sediments. Scalloped brachiopods (*lower right*) littered the ocean floor. The sea bed bloomed with tufts and huge honeycombed colonies of corals. Sea lilies (*background*) tossed their heads in the ancient currents.

The Fishlike Reptiles

By the Triassic period, which followed the Permian 230 million years ago, many reptiles that had returned to the sea had evolved into fishlike forms resembling the modern porpoise. These were called the ichthyosaurs, or fish-lizards. The fat, sleek Stenopterygius, four of which are shown gamboling above, was one of these ichthyosaurs. The long lizard tail has shortened into a powerful fin, and the slender legs, useful on land, have flattened into broad paddles. Like the porpoise, the Stenopterygius had lungs and came to the surface for air. Its young emerged tail-first from the mother's body over a period of several weeks. As it was slowly being born, the baby learned to use its tail to swim so that when its head was free it could rise to the surface for its first gulp of air. Ichthyosaurs had big eyes and probably keen vision. Sharp teeth were used in capturing the slippery fish on which they fed.

A Fearsome Sea Lizard

The hungry little monster shown opposite is a mesosaur, a spike-toothed, gap-jawed, tail-lashing reptile that swam in the waters of the Permian age, 125 million years after the Silurian. By the Permian, plants and animals had established themselves ashore and the land was soon to be dominated by dinosaurs. But the call of the sea is strong, and a few of the reptiles made the return journey to aquatic life, some swimming in fresh-water lakes and streams and others venturing into the open ocean. Mesosaurs were in the vanguard of this movement back to water. For all their boldness and ferocity, they were only 28 inches long. And for all their superficial similarity to crocodiles, they represent an evolutionary line long extinct. Their delicate bones are found in rock layers in both Africa and South America, indicating that these continents may once have been connected, or at least much closer together.

Climax of the Reptilian Age: Sea Dragons and Flying Freaks

The last great surge of reptiles was in the Cretaceous period, ending 63 million years ago. The land shook under the weight of the dinosaurs. Sea dragons like the 25-foot-long Tylosaurus (*below*) tyrannized the sea. And the air was dominated by an apparition which the ex-

perts have called the greatest freak of all time, the flying reptile, or Pteranodon. Pteranodon had a 27-foot wingspread, with parchmentlike skin stretched down the full length of its arms and its greatly elongated fourth fingers. Using these great wings to support a turkey-sized body with hollow bones, it glided rather than flew and returned to land only to lay its eggs. The Cretaceous ended and reptiles began to decline and die out. Today, only a few sea snakes, sea-going crocodiles and marine lizards represent their giant forebears in the sea.

3

The Underwater Landscape

Although most of our world's geography lies beneath the ocean, until a very few years ago man knew less about the submerged 70 per cent of the earth's surface than he knew about the near side of the moon. As recently as 1920, ships were still measuring the depths of the sea by heaving to and dropping a weighted line, a method that the Greek historian Herodotus watched sailors use 2,400 years ago. One single measurement in deep water could take all day. No wonder that few deep soundings had ever been made, or that knowledge of the land hidden beneath deep water was meager. The best idea that anybody had of the ocean floor pictured it as a smooth plain stretching for league after league. An occasional hollow or protuberance was known, but other bottom features, if there were any, were believed buried under muck accumulated through the ages.

The mysteries of the deep-sea floor were opened to man by an invention brought into use after World War I. This was the echo sounder, a device for measuring ocean depth by timing the travel of a sound impulse to and from the sea bottom. At about the time of World War II, continuous and precise depth recorders were developed and perfected. With the help of these new electronic instruments, ships could map the ups and downs of the sea bottom as they sailed along. Overnight, every oceanographic expedition became a voyage of discovery, and it quickly became clear that the ocean bottom was infinitely more rugged and seamed than had been thought. Beneath the sea were upthrusting mountain ranges and plunging canyons, towering volcanoes and dizzying cliffs. Lost in the eternal darkness was scenery that would match in majesty and grandeur the wonders of the continental land: trenches deep enough to swallow half a dozen Grand Canyons, cliffs long enough to stretch from New York to San Francisco, deltas broader than the Mississippi's, mountains taller than the tallest in the United States. New knowledge literally poured in to scientific centers, and it is still arriving.

The floor of the ocean is divided into three great domains. First there is the continental shelf, a shallow, life-crammed margin between land and sea. Then comes the continental slope, where the continents really end and the land plunges two miles and more to the true deep-sea floor. Finally there is the deep-ocean basin.

The continental shelves skirt most of the earth's coasts, sloping gently away from the shore to a depth of about 500 feet. Rivers and surf together built them. As time passed, rivers washed great loads of gravel, sand and silt onto the shoulders of the continental blocks. Then, when sea levels dropped because so much water was trapped ashore during the ice ages, the ocean's surf planed the deposits nearly flat.

Off many coasts, especially in the Atlantic (which has more miles of shoreline than the Pacific and Indian Oceans put together), the shelf is quite wide, often projecting more than 100 miles into the sea. The widest shelf anywhere stretches 800 miles into the sea off the Arctic shore of Siberia. There is no shelf at all off southeastern Florida because the Gulf Stream, running like a millrace, sweeps the offshore sea bottom clean of shelf-building debris. Off young, mountainous shores like the Pacific coast of the American continents, there has been little time to pile up much sediment and few rivers to do it. Consequently, the continental terraces are apt to be narrow or nonexistent. The shelves themselves bear witness that they once belonged to the land. Ancient river beds meander across them. With the help of special echo-sounding machines, ancient beaches and lagoons can be traced beneath the newer deposits of sediment. Along northerly shores, undersea boulder heaps and submerged fjords tell where glaciers once crunched across these platforms on their march to the sea.

At the outer edge of the continental shelves, the land plunges down, sometimes in an unbroken fall of two to three miles. These slopes are among

THE EARTH'S CRUST in cross section shows typical land and sea forms. The principal ingredient of continents is granitic rock, which is lighter than the basalt of the ocean bottom. As a result, the continents are believed to "float" like icebergs on the heavier material beneath them. Thus, if a land mass stands high, the crust below must be correspondingly thick. This theory, called isostasy, explains why the crust is thin under oceans and thick under continents.

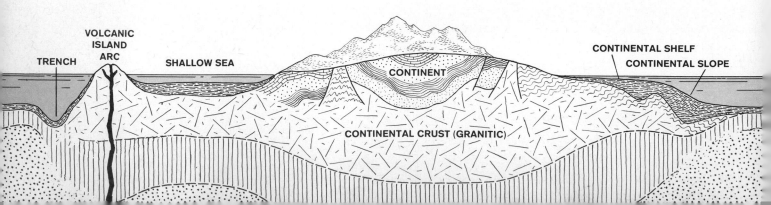

TRENCH   VOLCANIC ISLAND ARC   SHALLOW SEA   CONTINENT   CONTINENTAL SHELF   CONTINENTAL SLOPE

CONTINENTAL CRUST (GRANITIC)

the most imposing features of the entire earth; they are the longest and highest continuous boundary walls in the world. Where mountains crowd the coast and there is no intervening shelf, as occurs in Chile, the drop-off down the slope is spectacular. At one point on the South American coast, it goes all the way from Aconcagua, highest peak in the Andes, to the bottom of the Peru-Chile Trench, almost five miles below the surface of the sea. Within a horizontal distance of less than 100 miles, the combined drop from mountain crest to trench floor is more than nine miles—the greatest, most precipitous decline on the planet.

Nearly everywhere that oceanographers have probed the continental slope so far, they have found deep gorges and canyons cut into its face. What force had carved them was, for a time, unknown. Many were too far offshore, and in water too deep, to be explained as drowned river beds. Earthquakes had clearly opened a few of these gorges but could hardly have accounted for all of them. Authorities now believe that they were cut into the continental slopes by powerful undersea avalanches called turbidity currents. These are torrents of silt-laden water that flow down the slopes because they are more dense than ordinary water. An earthquake or an unstable overload of sediment on the continental shelf is enough to send a soupy cascade of silt rushing down the slope at express-train speed, gouging out a canyon as it goes. Turbidity currents can roll on for hundreds of miles, spreading out thick new layers of sediment as they lose force.

One notable instance of a turbidity current's destructive power was recorded on November 18, 1929, in the North Atlantic. A severe earthquake shook the Grand Banks south of Newfoundland and launched a torrent of sediment down the continental slope. In regular sequence transatlantic cables began breaking, first those highest up the slope and finally one lying on the ocean floor 300 miles away from the quake's center.

The deep-ocean floor begins at the foot of the continental slopes. It is far and away the biggest of the ocean's three geographic domains, comprising five sevenths of the total sea area, one half of the total earth surface. It is in this domain of darkness that man, using the ingenious tools he has devised for ocean research, has in the past few years made his most startling discoveries about the nature of the earth's hidden surfaces.

A logical, but nevertheless surprising, early discovery was that all the peaks, cones, ridges and cliffs reared beneath the sea have been preserved unchanged, instead of being worn away by wind, rain and frost, as they would have been on land. On the Pacific floor, for example, there is a cliff half a mile to a mile high and 3,000 miles long. It is as sharp and jagged as if it had been wrenched from the sea bottom yesterday, and yet it is hundreds of millions of years old. Even those few sections of the sea bed found

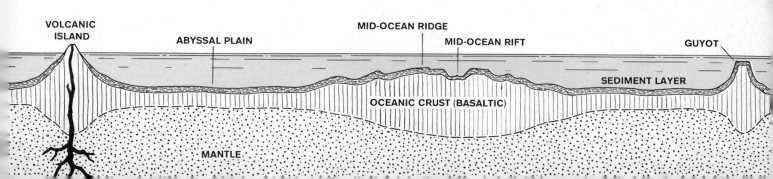

VOLCANIC ISLAND   ABYSSAL PLAIN   MID-OCEAN RIDGE   MID-OCEAN RIFT   GUYOT   SEDIMENT LAYER   OCEANIC CRUST (BASALTIC)   MANTLE

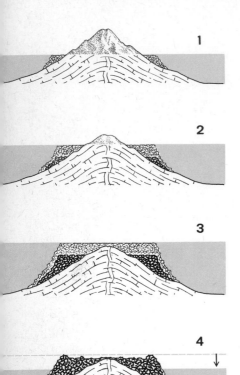

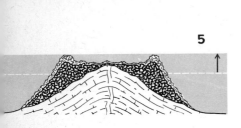

A CORAL ATOLL grows atop a sinking volcano in these six stages. The process starts when coral begins to grow on underwater slopes (1) and continues as the volcano sinks (2). In an interglacial period the sea rises (3) and a coral platform grows above the volcano. A glacial age follows and the sea drops (4), exposing the coral to wind and wave erosion. Again the sea rises (5) and new coral grows at the outer edges of the platform. Today the reef tips are above water (6), forming islands with a central lagoon.

to be flat turned out to be flatter than anything man has ever seen on land. Called abyssal plains, these level expanses lie smooth and even as a dance floor. The level of one such abyssal plain off the East Coast of the United States varies little more than one foot in a mile. Bottom cores show that this plain was formed by turbidity currents which, after carving canyons in the continental slope, spread out when they reached the sea floor and gently filled every sea-bed crevice with sand and mud washed down from the Carolina coasts.

Towering volcanoes, with a perfection of conical shape seldom seen on land, have been found by the hundreds, rising from almost every corner of the ocean floor. Here and there, as in the Hawaiian Islands, a few will rise high enough to jut into the world of light and air. Hawaii, though sinking, is still above water, but other volcanic islands have submerged again, as moatlike sea-floor depressions around them show. Some of these sinking volcanoes are responsible for what was once regarded as one of the most perplexing oddities of the ocean—the ring-shaped coral atolls of the tropical seas.

How could coral islands have anything to do with the tops of sinking volcanoes? In one of the most celebrated deductions in the history of science, Charles Darwin provided the answer in 1837. He knew that a coral reef is made of the limestone dwellings secreted by innumerable coral polyps and left behind after they die, one on top of another. From this, he visualized a coral reef as developing around the top of a mountain that was subsiding into the sea at just the right rate to keep the coral polyps house-building at their favorite level—the top 150 feet of the tropical sea. The theory remained only a theory for more than a hundred years, because nobody ever succeeded in drilling far enough into the center of a coral atoll to see what lay below the coral. But after World War II, United States Navy engineers did just that, sinking a shaft down through layer after layer of ever-more-ancient coral at Eniwetok Atoll. Sure enough, 4,222 feet down the drill hit into volcanic rock—confirmation of Darwin's brilliant surmise that if one only dug far enough one would find the sunken volcanic island on which coral polyps had first begun building, millions of years ago.

Half a dozen years before Darwin's theory was confirmed at Eniwetok, another geographical oddity was discovered by a Princeton geologist named Harry Hess, when he was in command of a Navy transport in the Pacific during World War II. With the aid of his ship's echo sounder, he spotted a number of volcanoes several hundred feet below the surface. The curious thing about them was that they had flat tops, as if somebody had sawed a large upper section off each one. Hess named them "guyots" (pronounced ghee-oh) in honor of Arnold Guyot, the late Princeton geology professor, to whose chair he has succeeded. Since Hess's discovery, more than 500 guyots have been located in the Pacific, a smaller number in the Atlantic. As to how they lost their heads, one can only conjecture, but the erosive action of surf may have been responsible. Ages ago, guyots probably stood above the level of the sea, where breakers could bite into the soft lava of their peaks. This hypothesis is supported by the otherwise unexplained presence of narrow fringes of round cobbles circling the tops of most guyots —all that is left of ancient stony beaches.

Other odd humps sticking up from the ocean bottom have been charted. These are sizable submerged banks which appear somehow to have become detached from the flanks of the continents and now stand like great underwater mesas. Most of these are off Australia and New Zealand, but the most publicized one is in the Atlantic. It is Galicia Bank, a flat-topped bulge of considerable size lying in 2,500 feet of water off the northwest corner of Spain. Its location gave rise to speculation that modern science might at last have found the fabled lost continent of Atlantis, which, according to legend, supported a rich civilization before it sank beneath the sea. In 1958 the British research vessel *Discovery II* dredged the bank and took extensive bottom photographs, finding nothing. No bits of pottery or stone tools, no signs of past occupancy by any air-breathing creatures were revealed. The existence of Atlantis remains unproved.

It may not be possible to find lost continents, but it is possible to make inferences about what may have been happening on some of the real continents. In 1959, oceanographers taking bottom cores in the Pacific off the coast of South America began encountering a layer of white volcanic ash in core after core. Further sampling in different places proved that a layer of ash was spread over tens of thousands of square miles of the Pacific bottom, indicating a period of immense volcanic activity at some time in the past. This was not surprising in itself, since there are many volcanoes in the sea, but there was surprise when the ash was analyzed and found to contain granitic materials. These proved that the source of the ash was a land volcano, since continents are made of granitic rock and the ocean bed is made of basalt. The only way granitic rock can get into the sea is for rocks to be swept there by rivers or scraped up by glaciers. Later, when the ice from the glaciers moves out to sea in the form of icebergs, it melts, and the few individual land rocks imprisoned in it fall to the bottom. Therefore, a widespread layer of granitic volcanic ash could mean only one thing: a prehistoric blast from the mountains of the land, probably the Andes, which may well have been one of the greatest and most devastating explosions the world has ever seen.

In the annals of world geography, the last few years are likely to be known as a second era of discovery, rivaling the 15th and 16th Centuries, during which much of the surface of the globe was explored. Of all the ways in which sea scientists have been extending their knowledge during this new golden age, one of the most ingenious utilizes a technique borrowed from oil prospectors, called seismic shooting. This technique, pioneered at sea by Maurice Ewing, the Texan who heads Columbia University's Lamont Geological Observatory, depends on the setting-off of explosive charges in the water to create little earthquake waves in the ocean floor that can send back information about the layered structure of the earth's crust. In seismic shooting at sea, two ships are usually employed. One ship drops the charges—often standard Navy antisubmarine depth charges. The other records the arrival of the sound waves coming in through the ocean bed.

Seismic shooting has helped measure the thickness of the sediments on the ocean floor, and has revealed that the earth's crust is only about three miles thick under the sea, as compared to the average 20-mile thickness on land. Shooting has also played a decisive part in determining the nature and the dimensions of what may well be the greatest single geographical discovery of modern times—the Mid-Ocean Ridge.

Imagine a single connected mountain range 40,000 miles long snaking through every ocean in the world. That is what the Mid-Ocean Ridge is. This is such a huge concept that although hints of its existence have been accumulating for nearly a century, the grand design of the entire system was not revealed until the late 1950s. One of the first clues came in 1873, when a rise in the middle of the Atlantic was discovered by the famous British scientific vessel *Challenger*. When continuous-recording echo sounders had come into use after World War II, other ridges were rapidly charted in other seas. Meanwhile, earthquake specialists had begun to notice a peculiar coincidence: the centers of many deep-sea earthquakes were located in these new-found ocean ridges. In 1956, Ewing and Bruce C. Heezen, also of Lamont, made two bold predictions. They said that a mid-ocean ridge would be found wherever deep-sea quakes occurred. They also forecast that the ridges would be found to form one giant interconnected submarine mountain range.

Since then, both predictions have been proved right. Extensive mapping by oceanographic ships has established that the undersea ridge runs right around the world. Equally significant, a giant crack runs down the center of the entire ridge. This crack is eight to 30 miles wide and more than a mile deep in many places. The great majority of earthquakes that take place in the sea are centered on this crack, which is clearly a place of critical instability in the earth's crust.

Theories about the origin of the Mid-Ocean Ridge, and about its monstrous fissure, are proliferating. Heezen has put forward the startling hypothesis that the earth is expanding, cracking right open along the rift in the Mid-Ocean Ridge. Another geophysicist, J. Tuzo Wilson of the University of Toronto, has calculated the rate of expansion to be one fiftieth of an inch a year—a rate so small that it cannot be measured. But, whether or not the earth as a whole is expanding, the evidence is before our eyes that it is stretching apart at certain places. We can follow the Mid-Ocean Ridge ashore in Africa, where it appears to become a chain of land mountains, its crack becoming the Great Rift Valley. Many geologists expect Africa to split in two some day along the line of the Rift Valley, but this may take a good many million years.

A more widely accepted hypothesis is that upwellings of molten matter deep in the earth (called convection currents) account not only for the crack but for the Mid-Ocean Ridge itself, pushing it up from below, and that all of the earthquakes found in the Mid-Ocean Ridge are part of this activity. But nobody is certain what is going on. The discoveries are too new yet. More evidence is needed, and much more time for thought.

The great undersea ridge does not exhaust the puzzles of the deep. There is still the enigma of the deep trenches. At first thought, it is entirely reasonable to assume that parts of the ocean will be deeper than other parts, and perhaps it is not too naive to suspect that the deepest parts will be at the points farthest from land. Thus it comes as something of a surprise to learn that the deepest spots in the ocean are all near land. More than that, they are located near *certain kinds of land*. Sometimes they are found lying off the shores of steep coastal volcanic ranges. More often they are associated with chains of volcanic islands, like the Marianas, the Philippines, the West Indies and others. Even more peculiar, all these island chains are near larger land masses, and the trenches always lie on the ocean side of the island chain.

The trenches themselves display a startling uniformity. Although some are much longer than others, they all have, in cross section, the shape of a deep narrow V. Most surprising of all, most of them are nearly the same depth—35,000 feet. The only exceptions are new ones still forming and some old ones which are filling up with sediment, but it is believed that if they were scoured clean they too would be 35,000 feet deep.

Puzzling over this evidence, scientists are beginning to grasp the outlines of a breath-taking idea. Perhaps trenches have something to do with the mysterious way in which continents are believed to grow. Nobody has ever had an entirely successful explanation of how continents grow and change shape. There have been theories that they drift around, but there are no scars on the ocean bottom to indicate that something as big as a continent had been dragged across it. Trenches supply us with a clue.

Obviously they are formed by some powerful down-dragging force. What it is nobody knows, although there are suspicions that it might be currents in the plastic material beneath the earth's crust, which wells up from the hot interior, then slides sideways and sinks again as it cools. It is thought that this sinking might drag the crust down into a deep V. At any rate, the trenches do occur outside volcanic islands. Gradually they fill with sediment washed down from the islands. When the trenches are full—and again for reasons not understood—their bottoms appear to rise again, pushed up from below. This pokes the collected sediments above the surface of the sea. A new chain of rocky islands appears outside the older volcanic chain. In time, the area in between is silted up, and a new land mass is born.

Some substance is lent to this theory by the configuration of the West Coast of the United States. Slightly inland there is a volcanic mountain chain (the Cascades and Sierra Nevadas) corresponding to an arc of volcanic islands. Right on the coast is another mountain range, which is believed to be the upthrusting of an ancient trench. The fertile valleys in between—Sacramento, San Joaquin and the others—form the area that was silted up.

Although there is no agreement among scientists as to why silt-filled trenches tend to rise, there is solid evidence that they do. An ancient trench runs for hundreds of miles along the East Coast of the United States. It lies 50 to 150 miles offshore, and is filled to the top with sediment. Without the aid of seismic shooting we would not even know the trench was there. But it has been mapped in detail, and its bottom has a pronounced upward bulge along one edge, as though it were rising. If the theorists are right, a new chain of offshore islands is forming there, under the ocean floor. In time, the sea between these islands and the shore will silt up. A good many million years hence, the eastern part of North America may receive an addition of land as a gift from the sea.

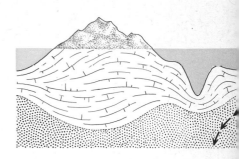

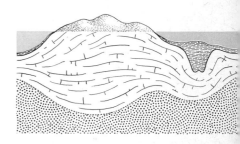

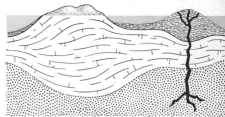

NEW LANDS and even new continents may begin to form as the earth's crust moves in response to a slow, mysterious current within the earth's mantle. This current is thought to flow horizontally, then curve down (arrows, *top*), sucking a strip of crust into a trench. Over millions of years, the trench fills with sediment (*center*). As the current relaxes, for reasons unknown, heavier rock framing the trench presses in, forcing up the sagged crust and the sediment atop it (*bottom*). Finally the former trench emerges as an arc of volcanic islands.

Portrait of the Sea Floor

Hauling up cores, bouncing sonar signals off the bottom, diving deep in bathyscaphs, observing submarine volcanoes, scientists are increasing their knowledge of the undersea landscape. From studies pursued during the recent International Geophysical Year have come dramatic increases in what mankind knows about the bottom of the ocean.

AN ISLAND IS BORN as a volcano emerges from the sea off the Japanese coast in 1952 (*opposite*). Sulphur fumes dyed the water yellow and poisoned a great many fish.

PROBING into the 4,500-foot Cariaco Trench off the Venezuelan coast (*right*), Woods Hole Oceanographic Institution scientists sample bottom debris with a corer.

The North Atlantic: A Weird Landscape of Ridge and Rift

Working closely together, IGY scientists of 66 nations from both sides of the Iron Curtain found out innumerable secrets of the 70 per cent of the planet's surface which lies hidden beneath the ocean. These remarkable maps, incorporating findings made during the International Geophysical Year and drawn by cartographer Kenneth Fagg, show a new world, the world as it would look with all water removed. On the map below, a giant submerged mountain

GREENLAND
ICELAND
Rockall Island
NEWFOUNDLAND
FLEMISH CAP
ANTIALTAIR SEAMOUNTS
GRAND BANKS
ALTAIR SEAMOUNTS
MILNE SEAMOUNT
MID-OCEAN CANYON
AZORES PLATEAU
LAURENTIAN CHANNEL
SOHM ABYSSAL PLAIN
KELVIN SEAMOUNTS
ATLANTIS SEAMOUNTS
Madeira Islands
HUDSON CANYON
PLATO SEAMOUNTS
CORNER SEAMOUNTS
CRUISER GUYOT
MADEIRA ABYSSAL PLAIN
Canary Islands
HATTERAS CANYON
MUIR SEAMOUNT
GREAT METEOR GUYOT
BERMUDA RISE
ABYSSAL HILLS
FLORIDA
BLAKE ESCARPMENT
HATTERAS ABYSSAL PLAIN
VEMA GAP
NARES ABYSSAL PLAIN
CAPE VERDE ABYSSAL PLAIN
MID-ATLANTIC RIDGE
PUERTO RICO TRENCH
Cape Verde Islands
CONTINENTAL SHELF
COLOMBIA ABYSSAL PLAIN
BEATA RIDGE
AVES RIDGE
ABYSSAL HILLS
VENEZUELA
DEMERRA ABYSSAL PLAIN
MID-ATLANTIC RIFT
BRAZIL
CEARA ABYSSAL PLAIN
St. Paul Rocks
SIERR
75 W
60 W
45 W
Equator

range, known as the Mid-Atlantic Ridge, snakes down the very center of the Atlantic and occupies a third of its floor. Studded with live volcanic peaks, the ridge's broadly terraced flanks thrust sideways to a width varying from 300 to 1,200 miles. A mighty crevasse, as much as 30 miles wide, splits the ridge's crest along its entire 10,000-mile length. Occasionally the pinnacles of this vast range poke above sea level as islands such as the Azores and Iceland.

At the base of the ridge are bumpy stretches called abyssal hills, which level off into abyssal plains. These lie about three miles below sea level and, with the exception of the 27,510-foot-deep Puerto Rico Trench, are the deepest part of the North Atlantic. Their monotony is broken by scattered seamounts (submarine mountains with peaks three miles high). At their edge the plains rise to meet the cliff-like continental slopes and the shallow continental shelves.

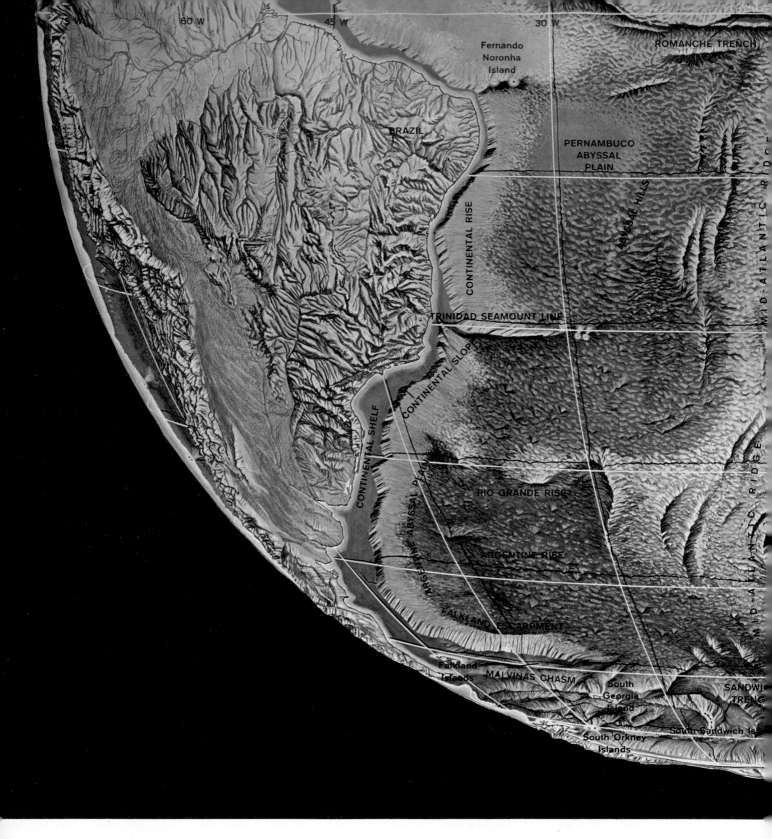

The following labels appear on the relief map:

75 W 60 W 45 W 30 W

Fernando Noronha Island

ROMANCHE TRENCH

BRAZIL

PERNAMBUCO ABYSSAL PLAIN

ABYSSAL HILLS

MID-ATLANTIC RIDGE

CONTINENTAL RISE

TRINIDAD SEAMOUNT LINE

CONTINENTAL SLOPE

CONTINENTAL SHELF

ARGENTINE ABYSSAL PLAIN

RIO GRANDE RISE

ARGENTINE RISE

MID-ATLANTIC RIDGE

FALKLAND ESCARPMENT

Falkland Islands

MALVINAS CHASM

South Georgia Island

SANDWICH TRENCH

South Sandwich Is.

South Orkney Islands

The South Atlantic: Silted Plains and Fractured Mountains

Plunging southward past the 25,748-foot-deep Romanche Trench, the great Mid-Atlantic Ridge swerves with the curves of the shelving continental shores and grows broader as it goes south. The smaller Guinea and Walvis Ridges branch off toward Africa. The mighty ridge strides on amid abyssal hills and the broad abyssal plains, thrusting the solitary landmark of Ascension Island into the South Atlantic mists. Knifing down the ridge's back is

66

Annobon
Island

MID-ATLANTIC RIFT

GUINEA RIDGE

CONGO FANS

CONGO
CANYON

EAST AFRICAN RIFT

A N G O L A
A B Y S S A L
P L A I N

St. Helena Island

RIFT
MOUNTAINS

MADAGASCAR

WUST
SEAMOUNT

WALVIS RIDGE

ORANGE CANYON

CAPE
ABYSSAL
PLAIN

UNION OF
SOUTH AFRICA

ABYSSAL HILLS

VEMA
SEAMOUNT

Tristan Da Cunha
Islands

SCHMIDT-OTT
SEAMOUNT

Gough Island

METEOR
SEAMOUNT

DISCOVERY
SEAMOUNT

Bouvet Island

ANTARCTICA

the same great gash as in the North Atlantic. This oceanic rift may continue into a huge, dry-land rift in East Africa, formed of valleys and big lakes stretching 2,500 miles from the Red Sea to Nyasaland.

In the Atlantic the abyssal plains flanking the ridge are the continents' dustbin, where currents drop silt from land. Sometimes the sediment crashes off the continental shelves in swirling subsea avalanches and may help etch out the submarine canyons, like the Congo Canyon, which cut the continental slopes. Occasionally continental slopes jut far offshore, then drop in sheer precipices, like the so-called Trinidad Seamount Line off Brazil and the three-mile-high Falkland Escarpment, highest cliff on earth. Near this great escarpment is the deepest spot in the South Atlantic, the 27,114-foot-deep Sandwich Trench. Closer to Africa, scattered seamounts punctuate the ocean floor.

67

The North Pacific: The Deepest Trenches, the Tallest Peaks

The bowl-shaped Pacific, whose northern half is shown here, is the biggest single feature of the earth's surface, bigger than all six continents put together. As IGY plumbings proved, its vast floor is even more roughhewn than the Atlantic's. The Pacific contains the earth's most stupendous heights and depths, the 32,024-foot-high peak of Hawaii and the 35,800-foot-deep Mariana Trench. It has hundreds more seamounts than the Atlantic, a score more mountain

ranges and many more trenches, and it is dotted with strange flat-topped submarine volcanoes called guyots.

Toward the center of the great bowl the ocean floor rises, culminating in the volcanic cones of the Hawaiian Islands. These tower higher above their base on the ocean floor than Mount Everest's 29,028-foot peak does above sea level. Running along the bowl's eastern rim near the coast of South and Central America lies a newly discovered feature, the East Pacific Rise. In the north this ridge runs into the Gulf of California, and some scientists think it continues into the North American continent, where it underlies the western United States. From east to west the Pacific bowl is broken by four gigantic faults—the Mendocino, Murray, Clarion and Clipperton fracture zones. These form great underwater fissures as much as 30 miles wide and 3,300 miles long, with cliff-like sides rising to heights of 10,500 feet.

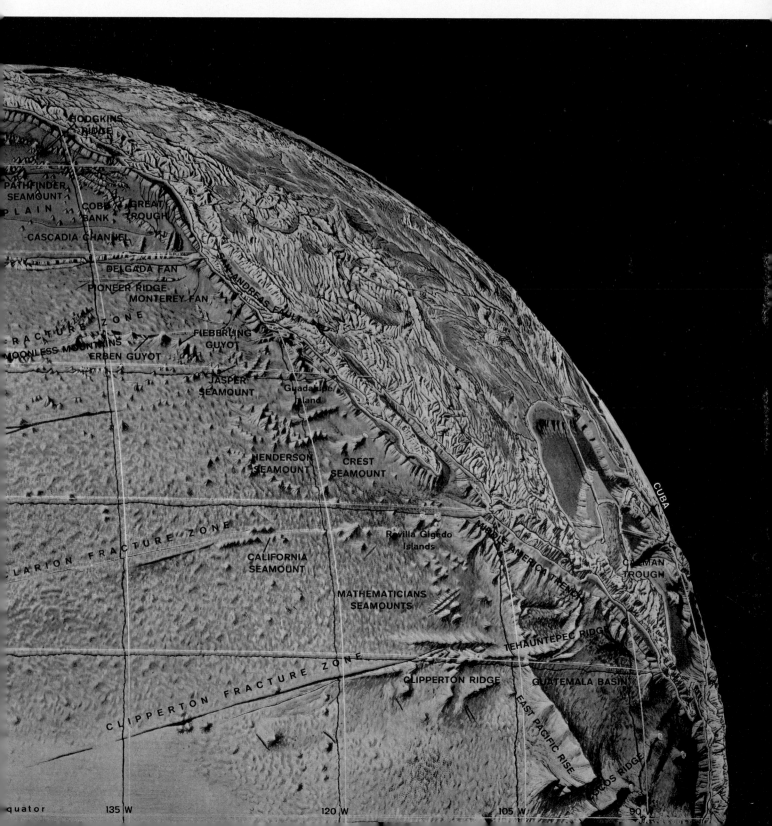

NEW
BRITAIN
TRENCH

NEW GUINEA

Gilbert Islands

Solomon
Islands

Ellice Islands

VITIAZ
TRENCH

Phoenix
Islands

Tokelau
Islands

Line
Islands

CORAL
SEA
BASIN

New
Hebrides
Islands

NORTH
FIJI
BASIN

Fiji
Islands

Samoa
Islands

DISAPPOINTMENT
SEAMOUNT
Tonga
Islands

Society
Islands

NEW
HEBRIDES
TRENCH

TONGA TRENCH

Cook
Islands

AUSTRALIA

New
Caledonia

SOUTH
FIJI
BASIN

Austral
Islands

Kermadec
Islands

KERMADEC TRENCH

NEW ZEALAND   CHATHAM RISE

Bounty
Islands

The South Pacific: A New Range
and a Mighty Trench

A submarine range of mountains loops from South America
around Australia toward the Indian Ocean to join the Mid-
Atlantic Ridge, making up a 40,000-mile-long undersea
chain, the biggest in the world by far. Off South America,
the summits of this so-called East Pacific Rise lie 10,000 feet
below sea level, except where they rear up into the Galápa-
gos and Easter Islands. During the IGY, scientists found
that the amount of heat flowing through the ocean bottom

near Easter Island is seven times greater than the typical heat flow elsewhere on the earth's surface, leading to a surmise that the rise is welling up with molten rock from the planet's depths and may someday be dry land.

The most awesome of the southwest Pacific's marvels is the Tonga-Kermadec Trench, 1,600 miles long and 34,876 feet deep, big enough to hold half a dozen Grand Canyons. To the north, Soviet scientists found the 600-mile-long Vitiaz Trench, near where U.S. and Japanese warships fought some of World War II's fiercest sea battles. The rest of the ocean floor is dotted with seamounts and domed hills 100 to 3,000 feet high, with tops two or three miles below sea level. IGY scientists originated some curious names: Disappointment Seamount was called that because two sets of dredging tools were lost there, and Bagel Seamount memorializes a homesick oceanographer's favorite food.

Man's Deep Dives to Polar Floor and Ocean Trench

Novel submersible devices have made it possible for men to explore the deepest and most remote areas of the ocean. A bathyscaph (*opposite page*) has descended to a record depth of 35,800 feet, and nuclear submarines have probed under the polar ice. In the Arctic (*map, right*), submarines found that the deepest part is the Eurasian Abyssal Plain, 14,700 feet below sea level. The sea is 13,560 feet deep at the North Pole. A big surprise of IGY was the discovery that the Antarctic (*map, opposite*) has a fifth less land area than had been thought. A 1,500-foot-deep sea channel beneath the ice cuts a slice off the continent: Ellsworth Highland and Marie Byrd Land are actually islands.

AFTER THEIR HISTORIC DESCENT TO THE FLOOR OF THE WESTERN PACIFIC'S MARIANA TRENCH, JACQUES PICCARD (BELOW, LEFT)

Map labels:

90 W

BELLINGSHAUSEN SEA FLOOR

PALMER PENINSULA

MARIE BYRD LAND

ELLSWORTH HIGHLAND

WEDDELL SEA FLOOR

PACIFIC OCEAN FLOOR

ATLANTIC OCEAN FLOOR

ROSS SEA FLOOR

ROSS ICE SHELF

Horlick Mountains

FILCHNER ICE SHELF

South Pole

QUEEN MAUD LAND

VICTORIA LAND

WILKES LAND

AMERICAN HIGHLAND

ENDERBY LAND

INDIAN OCEAN FLOOR

90 E

80

0

BATHYSCAPH "TRIESTE," being tested at San Diego, can carry two men in the ball at bottom.

... AND U.S. NAVY LIEUTENANT DON WALSH AWAIT PICKUP FROM THEIR SWISS-DESIGNED BATHYSCAPH, THE U.S. NAVY'S "TRIESTE"

4

SHOALS OF SAND that lie between
Muskeget (*top*) and Tuckernuck Islands
off Nantucket, Massachusetts,
shift their position constantly
under the influence of ocean currents.
Over a period of 60 years,
the deadly shoals around Nantucket
have sunk a total of 2,100 ships.

Currents:
On the Surface
and in the Deep

The waters of the sea are always going somewhere. This is true quite apart from the movement of the tides. If you dive into the surf at Nantucket, some of the water particles that cling to your back may have just arrived, after a many-year journey, from Antarctica 9,000 miles away. The surface waters drift—in mighty whirlpools half an ocean in size. The deep waters creep—in journeys that may take centuries to complete.

This restlessness is a trait of the sea almost as basic as its wetness. The best way to understand it is to take a long-range view of what the earth does in space. As it swings round the sun in almost circular orbit, it whirls on its axis in such a way that the seas near the equator receive the direct rays of the sun and consequently much more heat than the polar seas get. That fact alone would be enough to set the oceans stirring. When the sun warms the surface water at the equator, this warm water expands, and the sea level actually tends to be a few inches higher at the equator. This is not much, but it does produce a tiny slope. As a result, the surface water near the equator tends to stream "downhill" toward the North and South

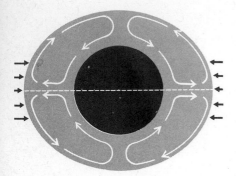

SUN'S RAYS heat the equatorial seas, which expand and flow "downhill" toward the Poles. The polar waters sink, flowing toward the equator on the sea floor.

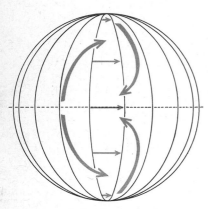

CORIOLIS EFFECT, caused by the earth's rotation, deflects winds and currents—to the right in the Northern Hemisphere, to the left in the Southern Hemisphere.

Poles. And the heavier cold water (heavier because water contracts as it cools, down to about 39 degrees Fahrenheit) sinks below the warm and tends to spread slowly along the bottom toward the equator.

The interchange of warm equatorial waters for cold polar waters is one of the most important of the ocean's movements. However, it is complicated by the sweep of other great forces which are also set in motion by the whirling of the earth.

As the earth spins, at 1,000 miles an hour at the equator, it tends to spin right out from under the oceans and leave them behind. Since the spin is eastward, the waters tend to pile up along western shores of the oceans. But that is not all. On wind and water, and for that matter on all moving objects—a boat, a ballistic missile or even a thrown ball—the earth's spin has a curious effect, causing them to turn slightly to the right in the Northern Hemisphere and to the left in the Southern. This is called the "Coriolis effect," after the French mathematician who first described it more than a century ago. Artillerymen have learned that they must make allowance for the Coriolis effect if they wish to be accurate with long-range guns.

The forces derived from the location and spin of the globe in space are basic to all movement of water on the surface of the earth. Laid on top of them is another, equally important force, that of the winds—winds set in motion also by the rotation of the earth.

The steadiest winds on earth are those at the fringes of the tropics, the trade winds. They blow diagonally toward the equator from an easterly direction in both hemispheres, and their unrelenting pressure drives the sea westward in great currents north and south of the equator. But the winds are just as subject as water to the warming influence of the sun and to the deflecting influence of the earth's spin: they circle, too. They curve north and south away from the equator and blow steadily back across the temperate latitudes in an easterly direction, pushing the surface waters from west to east—just the opposite of the current flow along the equator. Thus are set up the giant ocean-wide eddies of circling waters that form the main surface currents of the sea.

One of the first men to engage in the scientific study of ocean currents and proclaim their importance to mankind was Benjamin Franklin. He noted that American ships commonly took about two weeks less to cross the Atlantic than English vessels and asked a cousin, a Nantucket whaling captain, about this. He learned that American captains were steering so as to take advantage of a current running eastward across the North Atlantic at three miles an hour, and on their way home were piloting their vessels so as to duck this mighty eastward-flowing current as best they could.

Franklin thereupon had a chart drawn showing the course of the great river in the sea. And at the bottom of the chart, he wrote the words: "Gulf Stream." Franklin's chart, drawn for the benefit of all ships crossing the Atlantic (the haughty British skippers ignored it for the first few years), was the first systematic chart of an ocean current ever published.

To this day, the Gulf Stream remains the most intensively studied of all ocean currents. Now, of course, we look upon it as simply part of a great eddy, or gyre, as the oceanographers call it, that encompasses the whole

North Atlantic basin. This giant whirlpool movement starts with the North Atlantic equatorial current, flowing westward before the trade winds and carrying great quantities of water toward the West Indies. Part spills back across the Atlantic in a small countercurrent at the equator, and part is deflected north past the Bahamas. But most of it flows west between the outpost islands of the West Indies, like a stream coursing around the piers of a ruined bridge. Urged on by the incessant trades and funneled between Cuba and the enclosing Central American coast, the water piles up against the Yucatan peninsula in a head of more than seven inches. Blocked by this last land barrier and the mass of water trapped in the Gulf of Mexico, the equatorial water wheels sharply northeast and spurts out into the Atlantic between Cuba and Florida in what we call the Gulf Stream.

Riding past Miami at speeds of up to five miles an hour, this mighty stream, 50 miles wide and 1,500 feet deep, sweeps along more than four billion tons of water a minute, a thousand times the flow of the Mississippi River. At Hatteras, it veers northeastward toward Europe.

Off the Grand Banks of Newfoundland the warm blue mass of the Gulf Stream runs into the icy green waters of the Labrador Current drifting southward from the Arctic. The collision of warm and cold water throws up billowing banks of fog, thrusts long fingers of cold water into the warm flood, and slows the Gulf Stream's advancing force. The Labrador Current also brings hundreds of icebergs down each year, a number of them into the Gulf Stream and transatlantic shipping lanes. The Gulf Stream melts down 150,000-ton bergs in 10 days or less.

Halfway to Europe the great Gulf current splits. Part drifts north and east toward the Arctic. The other part of the stream turns south to join the North Equatorial Current off the hump of Africa.

Inside the ever-turning circle of North Atlantic currents is that strange region known as the Sargasso Sea. It may be thought of as the hub of the North Atlantic wheel—but a very large hub, measuring something like 1,000 miles wide and 2,000 miles long. Moreover, like most wheel hubs, it sticks out from the wheel. Sea level cannot be measured out of sight of land, but calculations indicate that the level of the Sargasso Sea is four feet higher than the water level along the Atlantic Coast of the United States. This is the result of a variety of causes, one of them being solar heating of the almost stagnant Sargasso waters.

From the Azores in the east to the Bahamas in the west, the Sargasso Sea is littered with patches of floating seaweed that have fascinated and terrified voyagers ever since Columbus' men, surrounded by the stuff, feared they were running aground. Portuguese sailors gave the region its name: the air bladders that kept the seaweed afloat reminded them of a small Portuguese grape called "Sargaço." Mariners long believed that the weeds could trap unwary ships, and as late as 75 years ago steamships were warned to stay away for fear of entangling their propellers.

Actually, though water movements may occasionally push together sizable rafts of the stuff, patches much larger than a household door mat are uncommon. And as a show of Sargasso abundance, the weeds—of several varieties, all cousins of the familiar algae of the seashore—are a misleading surface freak. Recent oceanographic expeditions have found that no other

WIND BELTS, affected by the earth's spin and solar heat, drive seas—from the east in the tropics (trade winds), from the west in high latitudes (westerlies).

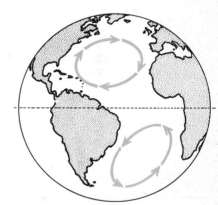

COMBINATION of three forces— sun's heat, Coriolis effect, winds— circulates sea currents clockwise in the Northern Hemisphere, counterclockwise in the Southern.

ocean area of equal size produces so few of these minute forms of drifting marine life, which all other sea creatures depend on for their food. Because of the pattern of winds and currents, little new water seems to enter the Sargasso from the big wheel that rotates around it. And because of the high temperature of its surface waters, there is not even any upwelling of colder water that could bring nutrient minerals from below. The Sargasso is unique, not for what legend claims it to be but for what it really is—warm, blue and terribly barren, a biological desert under its strange film of floating brown weeds.

In the South Atlantic, the North and South Pacific, and the Indian Oceans, there are similar turning wheels, though not all the circling currents are as strong as in the North Atlantic system. The current wheels of the South Atlantic are practically a mirror image of those in the North, since the southern currents, being on the other side of the equator, run counterclockwise. The northwestern Pacific has its counterpart of the Gulf Stream in the Kuroshio Current. Skirting Formosa and the Japanese islands, this big, slow-drifting stream delivers the same sort of warm, beneficent clouds and nourishing rain showers to the coasts of British Columbia, Washington and Oregon that the Gulf Stream bestows upon the coasts of northwestern Europe.

The South Pacific eddy starts with the South Equatorial Current, on which Thor Heyerdahl and his raft *Kon-Tiki* took their ride from the Peruvian coast to the South Sea archipelago of Tuamotu in 1947. The great circle is completed at the far south by the West Wind Drift through the "roaring forties," remembered from the days of sail, and on the east by the Humboldt Current flowing up the western coast of South America to Peru.

Oceanographers assure us that these enormous eddies—and the similar but ill-defined circling drifts of the Indian Ocean—are the main currents of the ocean's surface. Our knowledge of them is a product of generations of observation, especially since 1855 when a United States Navy lieutenant, Matthew Fontaine Maury, published the first world-wide wind and current charts. But the scientists are not nearly so confident about currents flowing undersea. They are just beginning to plot the course of some of the earth's deep water. In 1951 a research vessel of the United States Fish and Wildlife Service was in the central Pacific, testing a Japanese tuna-fishing technique known as long-line fishing, which involves the letting-out of cables several miles long with smaller fishing lines hanging down from them. To the astonishment of the scientists, this gear began drifting off to the east instead of to the west. A year later, Townsend Cromwell of the Fish and Wildlife staff investigated this phenomenon further, and traced the drift to a huge and hitherto unknown current flowing eastward immediately beneath the west-flowing South Equatorial Current. This submarine current turns out to be at least 3,500 miles long, almost as fast as the Gulf Stream and carrying nearly half the Gulf Stream's load of water. It has been named the Cromwell Current in honor of its discoverer.

On the heels of the discovery of the Cromwell Current came another, this time in the Atlantic. During the work of the International Geophysical Year in 1957-1958, a joint British-American expedition located a sizable current underneath the Gulf Stream. It was detected at depths of 6,600 to

9,800 feet and was flowing in the opposite direction to the Gulf Stream. Its source and destination have yet to be mapped in detail by oceanographers.

The vagaries of currents may have disastrous effects on life. The Humboldt Current, that mighty draught of frigid water that runs up the west coast of South America, shifts unexpectedly seaward at times. The result, for fish, for fowl and for men who make their living from its waters, is catastrophic. As it moves along the coast, the Humboldt Current carries with it a rich load of nutrients. A southerly wind stirs up eddies and offshoots on the shoreward side of the current, causing upwelling of water so full of phosphates and other fertilizing minerals that it nourishes one of the richest populations of marine life in the world. The current supports an extensive Peruvian fishing fleet. It also supports tens of millions of birds, whose droppings—guano harvested from offshore rocks—are the basis of a big fertilizer industry. Every few years, however, the southerly wind falls, the upwelling ceases, warm water moves in and the fish vanish. Millions of birds starve, and catastrophe overtakes the fishing and fertilizer industries.

It is known that the movements of deep-ocean water are governed by two main factors—its temperature and its salt content. At the surface, the ocean's temperature can range from a high of 86 degrees Fahrenheit in the Persian Gulf to a low of 31 degrees Fahrenheit or even lower in the Arctic and Antarctic. The reason this very cold water does not freeze is its salt content. Along the 40th parallel, the latitude of Philadelphia, surface temperature in the Atlantic can go from a shivery 50 degrees Fahrenheit in winter to a comfortable 70 degrees Fahrenheit in summer. But these variations in temperature are only skin-deep. A more accurate guide to true oceanic temperatures is found in a zone, or layer, beginning 100 to 600 feet below the surface and extending down to about 3,000 feet. In this zone, water temperatures gradually drop, even in warm parts of the world. Below it, the temperature of the water is almost uniform, hovering very close to the freezing point the year round.

We have already noted that cold water is heavier than warm and tends to sink. Salt can make water heavy, too. On the whole, the saltiness of the open sea stays close to 3.5 per cent. Near melting polar ice, however, it tends to be less salty because the ice that is melting is nearly fresh. By contrast, the water near freezing ice will have more than an average amount of salt since the ice that is in the process of freezing leaves extra salt behind in the water. This kind of water—both cold and salty—will sink the deepest. At the very bottom of the sea is found its heaviest water. This water is loaded with salt from beneath the Antarctic ice shelf. It rides the ocean floor all the way to the equator and across it into the Northern Hemisphere.

How long does the ride take? This is a difficult question since movement of deep waters obviously cannot be traced with drifting bottles, as has long been done with surface currents. Deep water is also much too slow to be measured with flowmeters. Nevertheless scientists have made calculations, and the wide spread in their calculations is a measure of how little they really know. Some estimate that it takes 300 years for a bit of cold, salty deep water to go from the Antarctic to the equator. Others say that it takes 1,500 years. By contrast, a bit of warm, relatively unsalty water may take only a year to make the circuit of the North Atlantic surface wheel.

A new technique may soon refine our knowledge of the movement of deep-ocean waters. Sea water contains carbon dioxide, which it gets from the air. Included in this is a very small amount of radioactive carbon-14. Like all other radioactive elements, carbon-14 "decays," or turns into a non-radioactive element at a fixed rate. This means that a sample of deep-sea water collected near the equator will contain less radio carbon than a similar sample taken in the Antarctic. The difference in the content of carbon-14 will tell how long it took the first sample to make the trip. Oceanographers look to such radio-carbon studies to tell us enough about deep-water movements to determine, among other things, whether it will be safe to put "hot" radioactive wastes into the sea.

Despite the layered stability of ocean water implied by the slow horizontal movements of the deeps, there are also regions of the sea with strong up-and-down movements. Water will rise toward the surface whenever it meets heavier water. It can also rise from moderate depths to fill a vacuum where surface water is carried away. Such movements are called upwellings. They are vital to the life of the sea and to man; they bring mineral nutrients to the upper layers of the sea, where most marine life dwells. The world's most important fisheries are to be found in areas of upwelling.

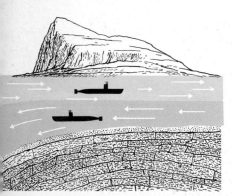

GERMAN SUBS in World War II, motors silenced, rode currents both ways through the Straits of Gibraltar. The Mediterranean's water, made salty and dense by rapid evaporation, sinks and flows outward through the Straits, while lighter, less salty surface water flows in from the Atlantic.

Mysterious as the tiny variations in temperature and saltiness are that set subsurface masses of water in motion, they can be spotted and even turned to military advantage. Early in World War II, while conducting antisubmarine-warfare drills off Key West and in the Caribbean, the United States Navy found that its sonar submarine detection gear often failed to detect submarines known to be down below. The difficulty was traced to temperature differences in the water, which bent the sonic beams, as light beams are bent in a desert mirage. Temperature inversion—layers of cold water above warm—can make the effect even stronger.

Scientists at the Woods Hole Oceanographic Institution thereupon developed an instrument, the bathythermograph for finding temperature zones beneath which German U-boats might hide. It was later used by the United States subs to enable them to hide from the Japanese.

There are also places in the oceans where a knowledge of how salt can make deep water move has been exploited for military purposes. In almost completely enclosed arms of the sea, saltiness can vary considerably from the oceanic average. One such area is the Mediterranean, whose saltiness (3.9 per cent) is second only to that of the Red Sea (4 per cent).

The average evaporation from the Mediterranean's surface is about 100,000 tons of water a second. This increases the saltiness and hence the density of the surface water. During the cool winter months particularly, the heavy surface water sinks and flows westward past Gibraltar to spill out into the Atlantic, where its salty particles have been tracked as much as 2,000 miles out to sea. The water lost to the Mediterranean through this outflow must be replaced, so lighter water from the Atlantic pours back past Gibraltar on top of the salty, outgoing stream. During World War II, German and Italian submarines tried to use these currents to slip past the British blockades at Gibraltar. Turning off their engines to avoid giving their presence away, they hoped to drift in and out of the Mediterranean on the currents. A few actually made it.

Rivers in the Sea

BENJAMIN FRANKLIN MADE THIS CHART OF THE GULF STREAM TO SHOW MARINERS HOW TO SAVE TWO WEEKS SAILING WESTWARD

Principles Franklin used in studying the Gulf Stream still guide scientists who work on surface currents. But the vast currents flowing deep in the seas are being explored by complex techniques such as those shown on the following pages. Oceanographers (about 500 in the United States) now include specialists in physics, geology, biology, chemistry and mathematics.

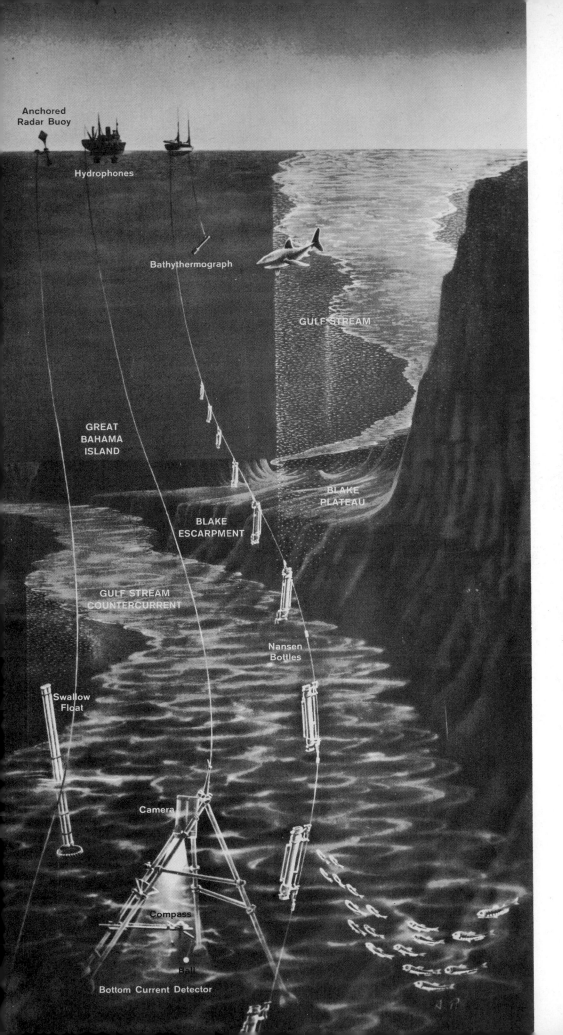

Anchored
Radar Buoy

Hydrophones

Bathythermograph

GULF STREAM

GREAT
BAHAMA
ISLAND

BLAKE
PLATEAU

BLAKE
ESCARPMENT

GULF STREAM
COUNTERCURRENT

Nansen
Bottles

Swallow
Float

Camera

Compass

Ball

Bottom Current Detector

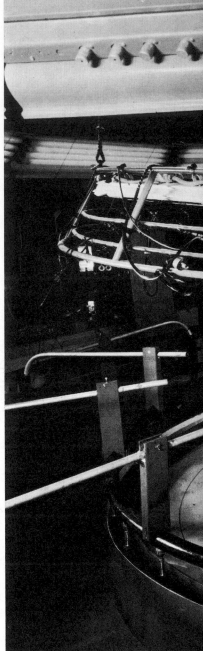

INGENIOUS INSTRUMENTS (*left*)
are used in charting deep currents. Swallow floats, fixed to
float at any depth, send constant beeps to surface hydrophones that track them as they
drift. Bathythermographs check
the water temperature; Nansen
bottles check salt, oxygen and
deeper temperatures. The view
is from the north, just off Blake
Escarpment near Cape Hatteras.

A DYE TANK AT WOODS HOLE, CAPE COD, SIMULATES WINDS, SOLAR HEAT AND THE EARTH'S ROTATION TO MAP THE OCEANS' FLOW

Charting the Currents

Oceanographers have devised new instruments and intricate techniques to study the constantly moving seas. The major forces that move the oceans can be simulated in a test tank (*above*) that rotates like the earth and has air nozzles to provide prevailing winds, lamps to provide the sun's heat. Colored inks, swirling against rubber continents, show hemispheric patterns of sea currents. Barriers can be inserted to show water motion in restricted ocean areas. To chart deep currents, the device at the bottom of the drawing opposite uses a rig of compass, ping-pong ball and camera. It shows the current's direction by photographing the ball's swinging.

Birds, Fish and a Cold Current Give Peru a Rich Industry

The cold waters of the northbound Humboldt Current each year provide vast quantities of fish for clouds of cormorants, shown feeding off the Peruvian coast. The seafowl nest on rocky islands, where their droppings and those of other sea birds accumulate as guano, a fine organic fertilizer, harvesting of which is a major industry in Peru.

Guano supplies are dependent upon the great current, which carries plankton to nourish the trillions of anchovies that in turn feed tens of millions of sea birds. The cycle, however, is interrupted in some years (six times in this century) by warm water flowing southward from the tropics along the Peruvian coast. The plankton perishes, fish vanish and millions of sea birds die. By 1909, reserves had become dangerously depleted, and since then guano harvesting has been strictly regulated. The islands are now sanctuaries for sea birds that eat three million tons of fish annually. Peruvian and Chilean fishermen compete with the birds for great catches in the cold offshore currents.

5

RETREATING SURF at
low tide exposes a rocky
California shore. Mussels
crust the rocks among
the tidal pools where kelp
and surf grass grow.
The rock in the background
has a wave-eroded tunnel.

Waves and Tides

Ever since man went down to the sea in ships, the rolling waves have fascinated and awed him. The greenish-blue breakers dancing on the shore fill him with delight; the black storm crests towering over a ship's deck fill him with terror. He reels before those most destructive of all waves, the so-called tidal waves loosed by undersea earthquakes. He feels the rhythmic pulse of the twice-a-day waves we call tides. It is possible that man's wonder at the moving sea is tied to an unconscious recognition that this is where he came from. At any rate, man seems to be a born wave watcher.

Most of the waves we know best are the work of wind driving against water. But notice that when a wave rolls over the sea, the water itself is not carried forward. Each particle of water stirred up by a

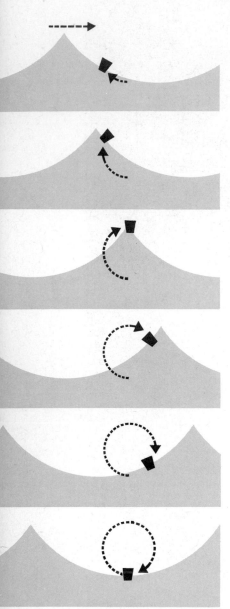

CORK FLOAT demonstrates that wave forms travel, but that the water itself does not. In these drawings, the waves move from left to right as the cork (or a water molecule) simply rotates in an imaginary circle, moving slightly to the left up the front slope of an approaching wave, then sliding to the right down the back. When the wave has passed, the float will not have moved more than an inch or two.

wave simply rotates in an ellipse that lifts it up, carries it forward a bit, then down and back nearly to where it started. One can observe this by watching the cork on a fishing line on a quiet day. As a wave approaches, the cork is lifted up by the wave's front slope, carried forward up to the crest, then back again as it slides down the wave's rear slope. When the wave has passed, the cork will not have moved more than an inch or so.

A wave watcher can observe waves in their simplest form by tossing a pebble into a pond and watching the even train of ripples fan out in a circle to the pond's edge. In the open sea, waves form much more irregularly than this. The wind makes wavelets of all sizes and shapes. They intermingle, they overtake and pass and sometimes engulf each other. If the wind is brisk, it will blow the tops from small, steep waves, forming whitecaps and heaping small waves together. When the wind is blowing up a confused mixture of waves in this way, it is called a sea. When the waves move out from under the wind that gave them birth, their pattern is called a swell, a regular surging movement which can carry thousands of miles. When waves roll ashore and dissolve in thunder, they are known as surf.

A wave expert can sit on the shore and, with what he knows of seasonal winds, offshore storm patterns and coastal contours, make a pretty fair guess at where the breakers are coming from. If the waves have a steep, choppy shape while still well out, they are young waves, shaped by local storms. But if the waves roll shoreward at slow, stately intervals, then rear high in a circling crest all along their advance and finally plunge into the foam with a booming roar, it can be taken for granted that they have traveled far, perhaps even from another hemisphere.

Often the big blue combers that break on the California coast in summer, rolling in from the south in crests eight to 18 seconds apart, have traveled 6,000 miles from their birthplace in winter storms east of New Zealand. Measuring the angle at which a big surf strikes the New Jersey coast, a wave specialist can say whether it came from the direction of Iceland or Spain.

How big the waves become depends on how strong a wind is blowing, on how long it blows and on a third factor that mariners call by the fine old name of fetch. Fetch is the extent of open water across which a wind can blow. A breeze of half a mile an hour can set in train a purring set of ripples. A four-mile-an-hour breeze will stir up real waves. But waves can only grow to a height of about one seventh the distance between crests without toppling in foaming whitecaps. To blue-water sailors, this means that waves close together cannot get very big. To coast-hugging landlubbers, it is also reassurance that no matter how hard a wind may blow across a narrow bay it cannot build up waves more than a few feet high.

It is on the open sea, where the wind may blow over a fetch of thousands of miles, that the biggest waves have been recorded. The sailor's rule of thumb says that the height of the wave in feet will usually be no more than half the wind's speed in miles per hour. In an 80-mile-an-hour hurricane, by this rule, the waves may run about 40 feet high. But individual waves may be far higher. Whipped together by a storm, traveling at different speeds, waves may combine in superwaves that can rise out of the driving, howling sea to rake the biggest ship. There is absolutely no rule about this —the old sailor's saw that the seventh wave is the one to watch out for is strictly a fo'c'sle myth. Most stories of big-waves are taller than the waves they tell about. But the wave reported by Lieutenant Commander R. P. Whitemarsh in the *Proceedings of the United States Naval Institute* is generally conceded by oceanographers to have topped all others. On February 7, 1933, the United States Navy tanker *Ramapo*, en route from Manila to San Diego, ran into "a disturbance that was not localized like a typhoon . . . but permitted an unobstructed fetch of thousands of miles." The *Ramapo* met it by running directly downwind. Soon after midnight the watch officer on the bridge saw, in the moonlight, a great sea rising astern "at a level above the mainmast crow's-nest." The *Ramapo* was then on an even keel with her stern in the trough of the sea. From these circumstances and the known dimensions of the ship, Whitemarsh made a simple mathematical calculation that gave the height of the wave: 112 feet.

When waves pass out of a storm area, they gradually lose height, and begin to stretch out the distance between crests to many hundreds of feet as they roll landward. The average speed of the ocean swell is about 35 miles an hour in the Pacific Ocean, not quite so fast in the Atlantic, where the fetch is usually shorter. When a wave finally approaches shore a startling change takes place in its inner mechanics. For the first time it feels the drag of a shallow bottom. Just when this takes place depends, curiously enough, not on the height of the swell but on the distance between crests. This distance is known as the wave-length, and waves generally touch down when the depth of the water is equal to half their wave-lengths. A swell with crests 400 feet apart will "feel bottom" in 200 feet of water.

As a result of touching bottom, the wave slows. Other crests crowd in behind it. Abruptly the circular paths of the water particles are squeezed together. The back of the wave, traveling faster than the front, overtakes it and forces it to rise in a peak. This peak, still traveling fast, tends to "lean" forward in a curl. Finally the wave leans too far forward and with a spilling, tumbling rush of water the crest topples into foam.

There is a handy rule for figuring out when a wave will break: it will do so when the ratio of wave height to water depth is about three to four. That is, a six-foot wave generally breaks in eight feet of water. A wave watcher can gauge the height of a breaker even while it is still far out by walking down the slope of the beach toward the water until his eye aligns the breaker's crest with the horizon. The vertical distance measured from the watcher's eye to the lowest point reached by the retreating water of the previous wave is equal to the height of the wave being measured.

Wave experts divide breakers into spillers and plungers. Spilling breakers, which have a line of foam tumbling steadily down their front as they

AN OCEAN WAVE breaks when it enters shallow water. In the diagram below, the dotted white line indicates the base of the waves. In deep water, the height of ocean swell (small vertical black lines) is one twentieth of its length (dimension A). In shallow water, the drag of the bottom shortens the wave length (dimension B) to twice the depth of the water (dimension C), and the wave is forced up into a peak (D). The peaking wave breaks when its height (E) is in a ratio of three to four with the water depth (F).

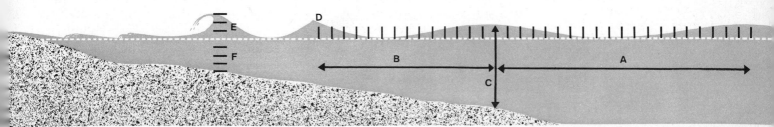

charge the beach, form on shores with gently sloping bottoms. The decrease in the depth of the water is so gradual that the wave will roll in toward the beach for quite a distance before it breaks, always on the verge of breaking but never quite doing so. These are the waves that surfboarders love because they give the longest rides. Plunging breakers, which collapse with a spectacular fling and a roar, are most often seen where the bottom rises abruptly toward the shore. They literally pound against the beach. Australians, who are among the best surf swimmers in the world, call them "dumpers," and avoid them as they would sharks.

Whatever the facts about the size of waves at sea, there is plenty of solid evidence that plunging breakers smashing ashore have engulfed lighthouses and shattered buildings anywhere from 100 to 300 feet above the sea. At Tillamook Rock, Oregon, on one of the most heavily battered coasts in the United States, waves flung a 135-pound boulder a hundred feet into the air and through the roof of the lightkeeper's house, wrecking the interior. Additional smaller rocks, hurled even higher by waves, have broken the windows of Tillamook Rock Light so often that a steel grating now encloses the beacon—139 feet above the water.

Despite such feats by storms, it is the everyday sloshing of the surf that does the sea's main job of sculpturing. In the course of a single year unceasing surf wears down and rebuilds thousands of beaches, alternately removing and putting back sand in a never-ending cycle, often placing it somewhere else. People living on the California coast between Santa Barbara and Los Angeles have seen the surf move great quantities of sand miles along the shore in a few years, robbing some towns of prized beaches and choking the harbors of others with tons of unwanted sand.

Surf owes its great power as a reshaper of coasts to its ability to move sand, and to the diverse ways in which waves and coastal topography may interact. When a wave passes through shallow water, it lifts loose grains of sand from the bottom. Because of the turbulence of the water in the wave's wake, the sand grains are slow to drop back. Moreover, the wave imparts some motion to the grains. So when they do drop to the bottom again, they settle in slightly different places from before. Such movement of countless millions of sand grains is forever changing the shape and position of beaches.

Along some coasts the shoreline is straight, the underwater slope uniform, and waves often come in directly at the shore instead of at an angle. In such places the surf simply moves sand back and forth from the beach to the underwater slope. During summer months fair-weather waves transfer sand from the slope to the beach, laying down a nearly horizontal layer of sand, called the berm, and building the beach outward toward the sea. On some beaches berm can be deposited at fantastic rates: 10 feet in a day, several hundred feet in a season. But it is all temporary. Once autumn storms begin, the sand will be carried back out to sea to the underwater slope, where it will be deposited in the form of winter sand bars.

Waves do not always roll directly at the shore. Often they approach it at an angle. But they have a tendency, the closer they get, to bend around toward the shore. This is because the part of the wave entering shallow water first is slowed by the bottom, while the part still out in deeper water races ahead—like a row of soldiers wheeling around a street corner. In

BEAUFORT SCALE OF WIND VELOCITIES

(1 knot = 1.15 m.p.h.)

Beaufort Number	Knots	Designation
1	1-3	light wind
2	4-6	light wind
3	7-10	gentle wind
4	11-16	moderate wind
5	17-21	fresh wind
6	22-27	strong wind
7	28-33	strong wind
8	34-40	gale
9	41-47	gale
10	48-55	whole gale
11	56-63	whole gale
12	64-71	hurricane

the case of a headland jutting into the sea, this action makes the waves bend around in such a way as to attack the exposed point from both sides. But this wheeling motion is never entirely complete; waves still hit the shore at an angle. This produces longshore currents, flows of water along the beach which can wash beach and sometimes even bathers right away.

Longshore currents can also set up rip currents. These occur when the longshore flow goes back out to sea through narrow, storm-cut gaps in off-shore sand bars. At such points the flow of water, which has been parallel to the beach, changes direction, and a swimmer caught in a rip current may find himself being carried out to sea, sometimes as fast as two miles an hour. In this emergency swimmers should not exhaust themselves by trying to swim against the current; they should swim across the current until they are out of it. Or they can let themselves be carried out until the current slacks and then swim ashore at a different point on the beach. Rip currents, incidentally, are not undertows. There is no such thing as a real undertow which will drag a swimmer down, although the backwash of a spent wave will sometimes give that effect.

Of all the waves that wash the world's shores, those which rock the oceans twice daily in response to the tug of the moon and sun may seem, at first sight, insignificant. That is strictly a surface impression. Unlike the winds, which only roil up the sea's top layers, the tides move the whole ocean. As a matter of fact, they move the earth and air, too. Every time there is a 10-foot tide in the water, the continents rise about six inches and the atmospheric blanket that envelops the globe bulges out toward the moon and sun to a distance of many miles. Perambulating sacks of salt water that we are, each of us is also subject to these waves, gaining and losing a fraction of an ounce in weight with each rise and fall of the tides.

People used to say that the tides represented the breathing of the earth. Now we know that they are caused by the gravitational pull of two celestial neighbors, the moon and sun. Of course the moon's gravity is much weaker than the earth's, partly because the moon is smaller than the earth but mostly because it is so far away. Still, this is enough to set all the oceans rocking as it swings on its daily journey round the earth. A bulge of water rises on the side of the earth facing the moon. An equal bulge forms at the same time on the opposite side. This is because the moon's pull is so much weaker on the far side that forces generated by the rotation of the earth and the moon around each other get a chance to push water outward there, into a second tidal bulge. The sun, despite its huge size, is so far away that its effect on the tides is about half that of the moon. Nevertheless, it alternately reinforces and offsets the moon's pull, according to its position. When moon, sun and earth are directly in line—as at new and full moon—the moon's and the sun's pulls are added together, and we have the unusually high tides called spring tides. When moon, sun and earth are at right angles to each other—as in the moon's first and third quarters—the moon's and the sun's pulls partly cancel each other out, and we have the unusually low tides called neap tides.

Unfortunately this is by no means the whole story; tides are a complex business. Because the oceans do not cover the whole globe evenly but are broken up into many differently shaped basins of varying depths, the

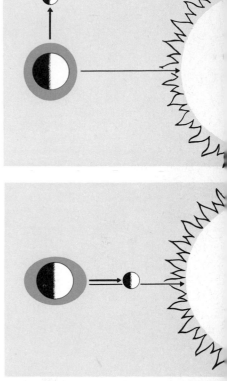

TIDES AT SEA are made by the gravitational pull of the sun and moon, either opposed or combined. When the sun and moon are at right angles these forces tend to cancel each other out, producing the small rise and fall called a neap tide. When sun and moon are in a line the pull is exaggerated, and extra-large spring tides result.

water in each basin will slosh back and forth in different ways in response to tidal pull. Thus islands standing out near the center of their tidal basins, like Nantucket and Tahiti, are apt to have tides of little more than a foot. Tides near the outer rims of particular tidal basins, especially in funnel-shaped bays along the rims, where the incoming tidal slosh has no place to go but up, are apt to be very high indeed. New Brunswick's Bay of Fundy has all these peculiarities, compelling the incoming waters to crowd into a constantly diminishing space. Also the sloshing in its particular basin coincides with the rhythm of the tides. Tides in the bay reach fantastic proportions, surging up twice a day more than 40 feet and sending a four-foot wall of water—the famous Bay of Fundy tidal bore—foaming up narrow, riverlike arms of the bay. All told, each tide carries more than 3,680 billion cubic feet of water into the bay, an amount equal to all the water consumed by all the people of the United States in three months.

When rising tides coincide with storms, they can cause frightful damage, as at Galveston, Texas, in 1900, when a tide rose 15 feet in a hurricane, topped the sea wall and drowned nearly 6,000 people. But the most destructive of all waves are caused neither by wind nor the tug of moon and sun, but by giant disturbances under the sea. These waves have long been called tidal waves, much to the annoyance of scientists, who point out that the waves have nothing to do with the tides. The scientists have not helped matters by adopting the Japanese word for them, "tsunami"—tsunami means large waves in harbors.

Tidal waves or tsunamis, they are caused by world-shaking earthquakes and volcanic eruptions beneath the sea. They cross the ocean in the form of low waves, so low in fact that ships at sea often do not know that a tsunami is passing. They flash through the water at jet-plane speed; averaging about 450 miles per hour, individual waves travel more than 15 minutes apart and the first one is not necessarily the worst. When they approach shallow water, they rise to overwhelming heights and hit with pulverizing force. They have been known to rise 60 feet on flat, low-lying shores, and more than a hundred feet at the head of V-shaped inlets.

Disastrous tsunamis have struck most often along Pacific shores. Japan has had 15 of them since 1596, including one in 1896 which killed 27,122 people. The explosion of the East Indian volcano-island Krakatoa in 1883 killed 36,380 people, wiping out village after village on neighboring islands. Krakatoa's tsunamis went all the way around the world, leaving their mark on tide gauges in the English Channel.

There is a good chance that such appalling loss of life may be a thing of the past. After 1946 the United States Coast and Geodetic Survey set up a network to flash warnings of undersea earthquakes that might send tsunamis racing across the Pacific. In the tsunami that followed the Chilean earthquake in 1960, many lives were saved when the network's warnings got through in time, but hundreds of others were lost, mainly when warnings arrived too late. The network is now being expanded as other Pacific nations join the United States, and improved arrangements have been made to flash warnings from earthquake-recording stations direct to threatened areas. Thus, by taking up still another kind of wave watching, man may learn to live with tsunamis.

Waves That Shape Shores

TOUCHING THE SEA FLOOR NEAR A BEACH, A BREAKING WAVE SLOWS, RISES TO A CREST AND THEN TOPPLES ON THE SANDS

The earth's hundreds of thousands of miles of seacoasts are daily reshaped by waves that are driven by winds, pulled by the gravity of sun and moon, and churned by submarine earth tremors. For each cliff or headland that is eroded by surging seas, somewhere a curved beach is being molded of drifting sands carried by the waves.

TIDAL BORES FROM THE BAY OF FUNDY SURGE TWICE DAILY IN A WALL OF WATER UP THE PETITCODIAC RIVER IN NEW BRUNSWICK

A TSUNAMI hits Oahu, Hawaii. Seconds after taking this picture, the photographer fled, the entire area, on Kawela Bay, was under water and 159 people were killed.

The Waves That Destroy

The power of ocean waves, whether caused by winds or by undersea earthquakes, is enormous when they strike the land. Year in and year out, the worst coastal weather in the world is in the North Atlantic. Engineers have measured the force of breakers on the coast of Scotland at 6,000 pounds per square foot. At one place a storm tore apart a breakwater by ripping away an 800-ton concrete slab, together with a 550-ton foundation to which it was bound by iron. The replacement section, weighing 2,600 tons, was promptly swept away again in another storm.

Most destructive of all waves is the tsunami (commonly called a tidal wave but actually the result of an underwater earthquake or volcano). The tsunami is a shock wave caused by the sudden displacement of a vast amount of water, and may travel great distances before striking land. The tsunamis that hit Hawaii in 1946 and 1957 were created by earthquakes that took place more than 2,000 miles away in the Aleutian Trench.

Tidal bores (*above*) result from the blocking of rising tides at a river's mouth by sand bars. The water builds up until it can break through to race upstream, usually in a single wave. Most tidal bores are harmless but the bore of the Tsientang River in China is often dangerous, with waves sometimes 25 feet high.

STORM WAVES from winds at sea destroy a house at Seal Beach, California. This was the waves' final punch, shattering the house and sending fragments 50 feet high.

DRIVEN BY GALES, waves strike Minot's Lighthouse (*opposite*) in Massachusetts Bay, sometimes enveloping the 114-foot tower. An earlier light was swept away in 1851.

GRAINS OF BEACH SAND are enlarged 64 times in this photomicrograph. These are bits of quartz, the sand type most resistant to erosion.

SEEDED BY WIND, sand verbena sprouts on a California beach. Sand will pile about it, more plants will grow and a flowered dune will form.

How Beaches Are Made

Waves work endlessly to build and reshape shorelines, wearing down rocks into pebbles and then into sand. The stones at left were worn smooth as they ground against each other in the surf. Their disintegration may take thousands of years, since they are now packed too tightly and exposed to surf too quiet for efficient grinding. One-foot rocks may become sand in a few hundred years if kept in motion. Sand thus produced contains fragments of many rocks and minerals. Some are soft and grind to mud or clay, to be carried out to sea where they settle in sedimentary layers. Others are hard, like the quartz grains shown above. Quartz decomposes so slowly that it is the commonest sand on earth.

The texture of sand determines the kind of beach the sea will build. Coarse sand is like blotting paper; waves sink directly into it, depositing whatever sand they may be carrying. It piles up loosely and is constantly being moved around. Steep beaches result. Fine sand packs much tighter. Waves do not sink in; their action leaves a smooth, hard, gentle slope.

ROCKS LEFT BY GLACIERS 15,000 years ago cover a Long Island beach. Waves have rounded them and will finally grind them to sand.

TWO VIEWS of a California beach show how gentle summer waves deposit sand (*center*) and how rough winter seas take it away (*bottom*).

MANGROVE ROOTS grip the sea floor on Australia's Great Barrier Reef, arching above a rounded brain coral (*center foreground*) and several dozen spiny sea urchins. The mangrove tree is a creator of land. It anchors itself on muddy shores or coral reefs, where its twisting roots collect debris and sediment in which other vegetation can settle and grow. The stilt roots shown here rise above the water and often intertwine with aerial roots sent down from the tree's branches. Mangroves thrive best in the brackish waters of creeks, marshes and lagoons. Their seedlings may drift at sea for months before wedging and taking root on a shoal to start the formation of another island.

SEA PALMS cling to rocks encrusted with red algae on the Seventeen-Mile-Drive, along the Monterey Peninsula near Carmel, California. The sea palm, a type of brown algae, resists the buffeting of powerful surf by resiliency rather than rigidity. Its flexible stalks, from 12 to 18 inches high, give way easily to the force of breaking waves, bending with the shock until flattened against the rocks, then rising in unison to full height as soon as the waves pass. Sea palms keep tight grasp on the rocks with a rootlike organ called a holdfast, of the same tough material as the stalks. They are found only on the Pacific Coast of North America, along rocky shores and flats where surf is rough and continuous.

IN A TIDAL POOL at Cape
Ann, Massachusetts, algae
cluster in three colors: red,
green and brown. The leafy
plants are a rockweed used
for food in the Far East.

GREEN ALGA in a tubular
form (*right*) grows in quiet
waters near the shore; here
it coats rocks on Martha's
Vineyard. A similar alga is
picked for food in Hawaii.

Vegetation of Sea and Shore

Algae, the simplest forms of plant life, are the ultimate food sources for
marine animals. Millions of creatures eat algae and are in turn eaten,
in a food chain culminating in the great fish and aquatic mammals.
Algae have no true stems, roots, leaves or seeds, but all have chlorophyll
and make food by photosynthesis. Their cells take in water and minerals
directly. Green algae thrive on sunlit shores where fresh water seeps over
rocks. Red algae (*left*) form scarlet crusts in tide pools, but they can also
live as far down as 200 feet, drawing energy from the sun's blue and vio-
let rays, which penetrate to that depth. Brown algae are fitted for shores
and for lesser depths, where their pigments absorb sunlight readily and
where their tough, leathery structures can withstand surf, sun and tides.

COARSE KELP FURNISHES INDUSTRIAL GUMS. IT IS AN IMPORTANT FOOD PLANT IN JAPAN

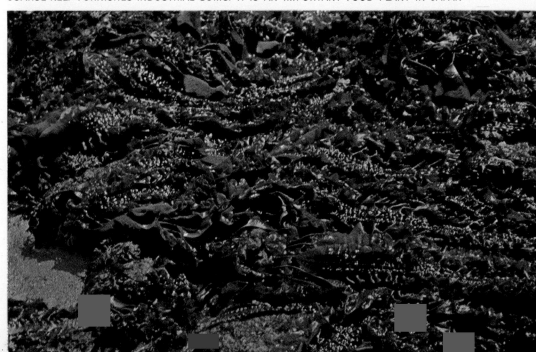

6

EATING A SCALLOP, a
starfish pries it open as a
codfish swims by. Experts
dispute whether the
starfish gets at its victims
by slowly pulling them
apart, or by paralyzing
them with a lethal fluid.

The Great Pyramid of Life

Life in the sea is extravagant almost beyond imagining—in its abundance, its variety, its antiquity, its oddity, its beauty and, balancing it all in nature's way, its mindless ferocity. The sea's inhabitants range from the trillions upon trillions of microscopic creatures that pack the blue-green surface waters to the 100-foot-long, 150-ton Antarctic blue whales—more than three times as heavy as any dinosaur that ever lived. They include some of the loveliest forms that nature has ever wrought—wonderful fish that are all silver and symmetry, animals that bloom like flowers while rooted to the ocean floor, glowing corals that spread in gorgeous terraces along tropical coasts. There are worms that grow 90 feet long, fish and shrimps that visit bigger creatures to remove parasites, fish that can change to any of eight different colors or patterns to match their mood, their company or their surroundings.

The sea is a great place for life. It is also a great place for leftover life— jellyfish, corals, sponges, starfish, horseshoe crabs and other living fossils that still flourish long after the evolutionary process has passed them by. As a place to live, the sea surpasses the land in several important ways—less changeable temperatures, more support against gravity's pull, and water so conveniently available that marine life forms can take it right into their systems and thus get both the oxygen and carbon dioxide needed for life and the salts and minerals needed for growth.

Two main circumstances govern the relationship of living things in the sea—the unbelievably lavish fruitfulness of marine life forms, and the utter ruthlessness with which the larger creatures eat the smaller ones. Somebody has calculated, for instance, that if all the eggs laid by codfish were hatched and grew to maturity, the Atlantic would be packed solid with codfish within six years. But nature does not let this happen. Only an infinitesimal fraction of all codfish eggs ever become full-sized cod, and wastage among other fish is as great. One sea creature in about 10 million escapes a violent death, and that usually inside another sea creature.

The community of life in the sea can be likened to a pyramid. At the base is a multitude of microscopic plants and animals. These support a smaller number of larger forms which feed on them; and these, in turn, a still smaller number of still larger creatures. Finally, at the top of the pyramid are the relatively few large fish and other sizable sea creatures which could not exist without all the other intervening layers of the pyramid to sustain them. A single example, given by N. J. Berrill in his book *You and the Universe*, reveals just how much life and death are involved in a single food chain: "A hump-back whale . . . which is far from being the largest of its kind, needs a ton of herring in its stomach to feel comfortably full—as many as five thousand individual fish. Each herring, in turn, may well have six or seven thousand small crustaceans in its own stomach, each of which contains as many as one hundred and thirty thousand diatoms. In other words, some four hundred billion yellow-green diatoms sustain a single medium-sized whale for a few hours at the most."

"Food chains of this sort," adds Berrill, "link most of the larger active animals with their basic food supply and the column widens toward the base. Not only do the numbers of the supporting organisms increase with each step down but so does the actual quantity of living matter compared with that of the more grandiose creatures nearer the top. The larger and the more elaborate the creation the more expensive it becomes to make and maintain."

It is now known that even the deepest and darkest corners of the sea harbor life. But a consideration of all oceanic life in the broadest terms will quickly reveal that the vast masses of living creatures are largely concentrated in three main realms: (1) the sunlit surface waters of the sea, inhabited by an infinite number of microscopic drifting plants and animals; (2) the shallow bottom near the shores where worms, shellfish and a myriad of other stationary or crawling forms swarm; and (3) the open sea, just beneath the surface waters, which is the domain of free-swimming fish.

ONE-CELLED DIATOMS have bizarre silicon frameworks that look like anything from golf tees to pillboxes. These odd shapes assist the diatoms in floating.

The best place to start examining life in the sea may be the surface waters, for that is where the broad base of the pyramid of life in the sea is found.

At sea, as on land, the whole animal kingdom depends on the plant kingdom for food. Plants alone know how to capture the energy of sunlight and use it in making the sugars, starches and proteins that animals live on. The seaweeds of the shores play their part in this process, but in the total chain of sea life it is a small part. More than 99 per cent of all plant life in the sea consists, not of what most of us would recognize as plants, but of microscopic particles floating in the upper hundred feet or so of the ocean, where they can get light and energy from the sun's rays. Though they cannot be seen with the naked eye, they are there in uncountable numbers—suspended in the water like the motes of dust we sometimes see floating in a shaft of sunlight.

These living specks belong to the floating layer of marine life called plankton, which means "that which is made to wander." Plankton includes all sea organisms, both plant and animal, too small and weak to do anything but drift at the mercy of the currents. Of the thousands of different kinds of drifting single-celled plants, many will live only in water of certain temperatures or saltiness: they may float with the Gulf Stream, for instance, but perish swiftly if swept off into an eddy of the cold Labrador Current. Most are about a thousandth of an inch in diameter.

By far the most important of these drifting specks are the single-celled algae known as diatoms, which constitute six tenths of all planktonic life. Each diatom is enclosed in a transparent crystal case that looks like the world's smallest pillbox. One droplet of sea water under a microscope can reveal a magical realm of tiny flashing bracelets, pendants, needles and anchors. Each infinitesimal creature manufactures its own exquisitely formed house from the minerals in the sea around it, building the shining walls out of the same silica that common sand is made of. Many have odd projections that make them look like thistledown and help them float in the water for the same reason that thistledown floats in the air.

Just as land plants depend on minerals in the soil for their growth, these tiny sea plants depend on the nutrient salts and minerals in the sea water. In the spring the oceans, having been deeply stirred by winter storms, bring to the surface a supply of rich bottom water. This, with the increasing hours of sunlight, rouses the diatoms of the plankton to an astonishing awakening of life. In as little as two days they may double their numbers, and in the fierce intensity of their growth they will spread a living carpet over great areas of the ocean. Hundreds of square miles will be tinged yellow or brown or green, as the sea takes on the hues of the infinitesimal grains of color contained in each of the plant cells. After a few weeks' time the upwelling of rich bottom water ceases, the supply of minerals dwindles and the diatom explosion comes to an end, but not until after the rest of marine life has taken off on a veritable binge of diatom-guzzling.

Ever present in the thick of the planktonic soup are swarms of equally minute animal forms, representatives of every phylum of the animal kingdom and including the fingerlings of thousands of kinds of fish. In addition there are things that are neither plant nor animal, but something in between. A typical plant-animal is the dinoflagellate, a one-celled living speck

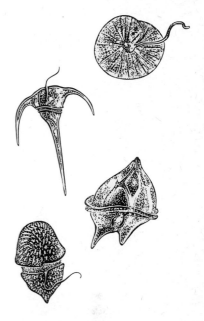

IN-BETWEEN CREATURES—half plant, half animal—are one-celled dinoflagellates; they either capture or manufacture their food. Whiplike appendages enable them to move around.

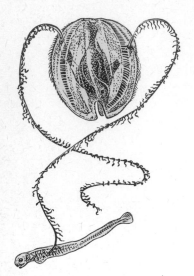

SEA GOOSEBERRY, a comb jelly common to all seas, lassos a small fish. Its sticky tentacles have a reach 20 times its one-inch length and can be reeled into two body pouches.

STINGING CELL of a jellyfish contains a long thread coiled like a spring, which shoots out when the needlelike trigger (upper drawing) is touched. The thread contains a paralyzing poison.

which acts like an animal in that it uses tiny feelers to beat its way through the water and eat other things, but like a plant in that it can manufacture its own food. Some dinoflagellates have the capacity to radiate the eerie glow of luminescence. When the wind sends a ripple of dancing light through the water on a warm summer night, or a splashing oar and moving boat trail a dimly glowing wake, it is dinoflagellates that give off the light. You cannot see them but you can see the light—a chemical reaction touched off in these organisms by the disturbance of the sea.

In those seasons when dinoflagellates glow and diatoms bloom, swarms of tiny, shrimp-like copepods spread across the sea's surface to devour them. Though they are among the smallest of the crustaceans, the copepods are larger than diatoms or dinoflagellates, and much more complex in their structure. They are probably the most numerous multicelled organisms in the world; in fact, they may well outnumber all other multicelled creatures together. They got their name, which means "oar-footed," from the jerky way in which they use their forelimbs to swim. Most copepods are about as big as a pinhead; still, they are a prime food source for larger creatures, from the smallest sardines to the biggest whales.

Copepods in fact are so important in the marine food chain that any other planktonic creatures that snatch them out of the mouths of herring and other commercial fish are regarded as enemies by the men of the trawlers and seiners. Two notoriously bad actors are the arrowworm and the comb jelly. One arrowworm, which is about three quarters of an inch long and perfectly transparent, has a way of suddenly darting forward and snapping up a copepod like a lizard catching a fly. In the same lightning fashion, it grabs and gobbles young herring almost as big as itself—looking much like a herring wrapped in cellophane at the most murderous point of the process. The commonest comb jelly is a round blob the size of a blackberry, fringed with eight comblike rows of hairs that can flail like Roman galley oars to drive it up, down or sideways. Snaring the freshly hatched herring with long, trailing tentacles, comb jellies can make heavy inroads not only into stocks of herring but also into the copepods that the herring feed on.

Another pair of tentacled drifters that have been making a killing in the plankton are the jellyfish and the Portuguese man-of-war. Some jellyfish are too small to be seen; others are as big as bedspreads. In some respects they are among the simplest of animals, lacking central nervous systems and many of the other organs common to more highly developed creatures. Yet the tentacles of the jellyfish carry stinging cells that are among the most complicated found anywhere in the whole animal kingdom. These cells can paralyze and kill fish as large as the jellyfish itself. The Portuguese man-of-war, whose ballooning float and sail made it look like a ship of the line to sailors of old, is not one animal but a colony of them. It is typically made up of several hundred individual animals of at least four different kinds that have somehow joined forces. A single animal of one kind forms the float; each fishing tentacle belongs to an animal of a second kind; a third kind of animal digests the food; and a fourth kind, quite distinct from the others, carries out the task of reproduction. Scientists have yet to unravel the puzzle of how these composite creatures came to be. They are also a bit nonplused about another peculiarity of the Portuguese man-of-war: its sting is apparently toxic to all creatures but two. A small, gaudy fish called Nomeus lives among the man-of-war's tentacles, impervious to their sting, and gets its share of every victim its host kills. The loggerhead turtle evidently just does not mind the sting. Fishermen have seen these turtles, their eyes swollen nearly shut with stings, imperturbably munching their way through patches of Portuguese man-of-war.

Altogether, no one knows how many living creatures of all kinds may be drifting in the plankton layers of the sea. No net has yet been devised fine enough to hold the smallest and yet deft enough to catch the swiftest life forms of the surface. Alister Hardy of Oxford University, an expert on this subject, says that just trying to record the number "would wear out the nought on a typewriter." Of diatoms alone there may be as many as several million in a single quart of surface water. Or take krill, the two-inch-long shrimplike crustacean of the Antarctic that blue whales eat. Willis E. Pequegnat of the National Science Foundation calculates that young blue whales, which grow at a rate of 90 pounds a day, tuck away about three tons of krill every 24 hours. Since the blue whale apparently feeds only during the six months it spends each year in Antarctic waters, that adds up to some 500 tons of krill per whale per year. Back in the days before whalers hunted the blue whale, says Pequegnat, there were enough of these giants cruising the Antarctic to consume 270 million tons of krill a year. Obviously, since the krill and the whales both survived, that could have been only a fraction of the Antarctic's output of krill. This year, according to Pequegnat's calculations, the Antarctic will spawn a billion and a half tons of krill—that is, 1,100 trillion of these planktonic creatures.

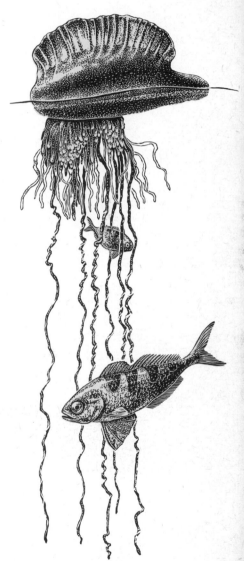

FLOATING COLONY, the Portuguese man-of-war is not one but many different animals that live together and divide the work of feeding, floating, stinging and reproducing. Nomeus, the fish, is immune to its poison.

The second great domain of life in the sea is the shallow bottom along the shores. There, where sunlight can touch the sea all the way down, the thick planktonic chowder extends right to the bottom. The coastal shelf is also the one place where plants grow from the sea floor, thereby adding to the food supply for other living things.

The food supply at the bottom of these shallow seas, in fact, is so rich that all the inhabitants have to do is simply open their mouths and eat. The food just rains down, pelting every creature with its bounty. In this paradise of plenty, life's major problem is finding a place—any place—to anchor and wait for food to drop. Just how thick a population can get was shown a few years ago when British scientists made a count of a single kind of bottom dweller, the brittle star, a cousin of the starfish. From samplings in an area off England's south coast, they calculated that there were 250 million brittle stars per square mile.

Many of these creatures, having once found sea-floor space, hold aloft clusters of bright tentacles to catch the nourishing rain of food. These are the animals that look like flowers and bear such greenhouse names as sea peach and sea lily. Some, like the sea anemone, may move slightly from day to day. Others, like sponges and oysters, must settle down for good as stationary soup-strainers, pumping the food-laden water in and out of their digestive cavities. In these creatures, only the larval forms retain the power to move or drift, which ensures the dispersal of their kind.

In this great world of plenty the rules are: eat, spawn and be eaten. A lowly sea urchin has rasps on its mouth so hard that it can bite off bits of rock along with the algae clinging to the rock. Other creatures have drills for boring holes through mussel shells to eat the mussel inside. The scallop, one of the brighter bivalves, has 30 to 40 eyes that can see such danger coming, and alertly moves away. Not so the clam, which must rely on its ability to bury itself in the mud of the bottom, and then extend a long neck unobtrusively in search of food. If danger threatens, the clam pulls in its neck and digs itself deeper into the mud with jets of water. How fast it can do this will be attested to by clammers on the West Coast who must dig furiously to keep up with the big "gooeyduck" common there. An exposed clam, however, has no defense against the starfish. Nor, in fact, has any bivalve. Whether the starfish simply pries a shell open by relentless pressure, or whether it weakens its prey by using lethal chemicals, is the subject of a lively current biological controversy. In either case, as soon as the shell relaxes the least bit, the starfish extrudes its own stomach right into the crack and begins digesting its victim before it has even finished with the job of prying it open.

All kinds of bizarre marine life, large and small, turn up on the shallow bottoms to eat the food that falls there—or to eat the eaters. In sandy areas, worms burrow through the bottom, poking in search of a particle of organic matter that may somehow have slipped down past the massed mouths above. On muddy bottoms, sea cucumbers push along, slowly scooping the organic slime into their mouths and licking their tentacle fingers like boys eating jam. When suddenly attacked, some cucumbers cough up their entrails and, leaving them behind to distract the foe, slip away and grow new ones.

The skein of life lies thick and rank on these crowded continental shelves. But farther out, where the ocean floor falls away to greater depths, life thins to a thread. Going down beneath the surface of the sea, one reaches the "timberline" more quickly than when going up on dry land: plant life dies away at depths of only a few hundred feet, where the sunlight fades along the sloping ocean floor. From there on to the deepest depths, there is less and less food. Bottom dwellers have been found in the deepest places of the sea, making a thin living scavenging bits of organic matter drifting down from above. Otherwise, the rich life of the ocean bottom ends with the outer limits of the continental shelves.

The third great realm of marine life is found in the wide areas of the open sea, just beneath the planktonic surface layer. In the early days of life in the sea, all creatures drifted in the ocean's upper layers or crawled on the bottom. The vast space in between was not and could not be occupied by the types that then existed. The open sea was not claimed until a new kind of marine creature was evolved, big and strong enough to move about in the great waters regardless of tides and currents. Today the open sea belongs to those streamlined, neckless, water-breathing, backboned animals called fish.

Fish probably evolved in the shelter of rivers and lakes, and only later came down to the sea. Whales, dolphins and a few other mammals have joined them, and marine turtles and even a few sea snakes also range the oceans. But only a handful of creatures without backbones, such as the squid and the larger octopuses, have found ways to raise themselves to the ranks of the free swimmers of the sea. Otherwise, the open sea is the domain of the bony fish. They far outnumber their primitive cousins, the sharks and rays, which have skeletons of cartilage instead of bone.

Though there are over 20,000 known species of bony fish, counting both sea and fresh-water forms, the requirements of life in the open sea have not allowed very wide departure from a common basic design. Fish of the great ocean spaces need keen senses and protective coloration to survive in a world where there is no place to hide. Nearly all open-sea fish carry the colors of the waters they live in. Because the sea from above looks blue or green, those are the colors of their backs. Because the surface waters from below look silvery or whitish, those are the colors of their undersides.

Above all, open-sea fish must stick close to the cigar shape that allows them to move most efficiently through such a dense medium as water. Some of the most exquisitely developed of the fish that swim near the surface can travel through water faster and longer than many hulking animals can drag themselves across the land. Sailfish have been clocked at 50 miles an hour, flying fish work up to take-off speeds of 35 miles an hour, and marlin and tuna, at least for short distances, can go even faster. Tuna evidently can swim at a steady nine miles an hour indefinitely, and they never stop. It has been estimated that a 15-year-old tuna must have traveled a million miles since its birth. No other creatures of the sea can perform with anything like the efficiency of these living projectiles. The most powerful of the spineless swimmers, the giant squid, shoots along backward at quite a fair speed by jetting water from its rocket-shaped body, but its movements cannot compare in grace and staying power with the smooth trajectory of the fish.

A few fish, like the one-ton cartwheel-shaped ocean sunfish, the almost arthritically stiff-bodied deep-sea boxfish and the fancier little goldfish with their floppy tails, must rely on their fins to move them forward through the water. But the typical ocean fish uses its fins just for steering, steadying and stopping. Its entire body and tail are one long series of muscles which are the engine that drives this efficient vessel. It obtains extra power and speed by pumping water through its gills.

A fish has marvelously refined sense and control organs. It has special spots sensitive to pressure and sound along the sides of its body to help guide it by informing it of changes in the surrounding water. In addition, most fish have small organs called statocysts, inner cavities lined with delicate hairs and containing some loose objects like a few grains of sand. Its statocysts tell a fish, even in the blackness of the abyss, whether it is right side up or upside down.

Though gravity is far less bothersome to sea creatures than to land dwellers, the bones and muscles of fish are heavier than water and the fish have to do something to keep from sinking to the bottom. Mackerel, tuna and some other fish seem to stay afloat by swimming constantly. Others, like the cyclothone, a common mid-ocean variety, have layers of fat that hold them up. Most fish are kept from sinking by a centrally located swim bladder, an organ like a small balloon that is filled with gas

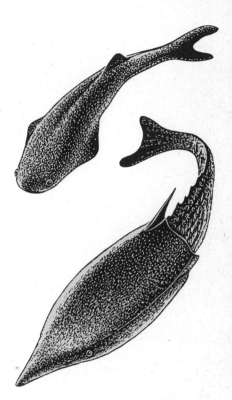

VERTEBRATE ANCESTORS were Thelodus (*top*) and Pteraspis (*bottom*), a pair of ancient fish. They swam the primeval seas 400 million years ago. Heavily armored and with primitive sucking mouths, they failed to survive the competition of more advanced forms with hinged jaws.

drawn largely from oxygen in the fish's blood stream. But these air tanks, unlike those of a man-made submarine, cannot be quickly filled or emptied as the fish moves up or down. In this one respect, the man-made submarine is more efficient than the fish. Most fish caught at depths of more than a few score feet are dead when hauled to the surface: the rapidly lessening pressure of the water on the swim bladder makes the bladder expand, rupturing the fish's internal organs.

Although fish have no vocal organs, they are by no means silent. When World War II vessels equipped with sensitive underwater listening devices reported hearing all sorts of strange beeps, grunts and groans, the Navy first thought they came from other ships. Later the listeners found to their astonishment that marine animals were responsible, that in fact the underwater world is quite a noisy place. Fish make sounds by grinding their teeth or by setting up vibrations in certain organs such as the swim bladder. Some of the croaks are believed to be mating calls, others warning signals passed back and forth among members of a school of fish. Commercial fishermen have tried to take advantage of all these sounds by lowering hydrophones over the sides of their boats in order to locate schools of fish. But most of the commercially valuable fish proved to be the least loquacious. Furthermore, all species have a tendency to keep quiet in close proximity to boats.

Since fish have no eyelids and, like airplanes, have to keep moving to stay in trim, marine biologists have never been able to satisfy themselves about how fish sleep. Some fish, such as the wrasse, appear to bed down at night; at least they cover themselves with sand and retire. Flounders and sole often lie flat on the sea floor and could presumably sleep there. Other fish can wedge themselves into crevices for the night. Certain small surface swimmers sometimes seem to bask in surface seaweed. But as for such open-sea species as the tuna, nobody seems to know if they ever fall into the state of torpor and suspended consciousness that we call sleep.

Another unanswered question is whether fish age. Some scientists think that in many creatures the processes of aging and growing may be linked, and that when growing stops, deterioration sets in. They suspect that in some aquatic animals, relatively freed by the buoyancy of water from the limits on size imposed by gravity's tug, growth never really stops. In that case they would not age as the rest of us do, but would slowly get bigger and bigger. It is presently impossible to test this theory, however, because the eat-and-be-eaten environment of the sea gives almost no fish a chance to survive to "old" age. And any fish that is not eaten apparently succumbs sooner or later to disease.

It has already been noted that the fish of the open sea vary surprisingly little in form from the torpedo shape of streamlined efficiency. But for fish, as for everything else, habitat regulates form. Thus, many of the fish that live among tropical coral reefs or along sandy shores have taken startlingly different shapes to suit their special worlds. The sea robin has outsize pectoral fins on which it "walks" the bottom, feeling for hidden mollusks and crabs to eat. The flounder starts life as a pancake on edge, with an eye on each side and a mouth in front. But as it grows, it becomes a horizontal pancake. Its mouth twists around toward the bottom and both its eyes wind up on top. Thus it can grub in the sand for food while it keeps a sharp lookout aloft.

Many bottom-living fish are able to change their color. Their skins are equipped with pigment cells that can either reveal or conceal the pigment, depending on which best matches the bottom they are resting on. The fish has no voluntary control over this trait. It is triggered off automatically by nerves in some fish, and by pituitary hormones in others.

Although the greatest concentrations of marine life are found near shore and in the sunlit surface waters of the sea, there is a vast area of perpetual darkness beneath the surface inhabited both by deeper-going animal plankton and by the fish that feed on it—and on each other. These fish are relatively thinly scattered through the depths because food is scarce down there, but their habitat is so vast that their total numbers are enormous. They are an odd-looking collection. Unlike silvery surface fish, they are usually dark in color: red, brown or black. Skeletons are light, tissues fragile and muscle layers thin, indicating that the fish are not very powerful swimmers, but survive in other ways. This is borne out by their mouths, which are gaping and equipped with long, needlelike teeth. Anything they can get their teeth into is a potential meal. One species, the viperfish, has such long teeth that they remain outside when its mouth is closed. Others have expandable stomachs, permitting them to swallow victims larger than they are.

Finding mates in this stygian realm is difficult. One species has solved the problem by allowing the six-inch male to attach itself to the three-foot female and share the latter's digestive system. Others recognize each other—and potential enemies—with lights. Surprisingly enough, in the blackest of the deep waters, most have not only kept their sight but can make their own light—by much the same process as fireflies. At times, says Dr. George L. Clarke of the Woods Hole Oceanographic Institution and Harvard, who has dipped a light-recording meter into the deep ocean waters, the depths resemble Fourth of July displays, lighting up in flashes at the rate of five a second.

One angler fish trolls 5,000 feet down with a fishing rod twice as long as itself dangling ahead of its mouth, a light organ twinkling at the tip. Another angler fish mounts its light organ inside its mouth, right behind the teeth. Still another deep-dwelling prowler not only wears patches of luminous bacteria below its eyes but has folds of skin which it can pull down like window blinds when it pleases. Some of these hunters can cast a beam of light two feet or more. Certain varieties of lantern fish have rows of lights along their sides like an airliner's windows at night.

Lantern fish, a large family of small fish, may play a role in clearing up one of the modern mysteries of the sea—the riddle of the "deep scattering layer." When ships first began using echo sounders widely, they kept getting "false bottom" echoes from several hundred feet down in places where they knew the bottom was thousands of feet down. Then it was found that these strange returns occurred only by day. At sunset the "deep scattering layer," as oceanographers called it because it scattered the echoes, began moving rapidly upward. Within a few hours it merged into the surface and was lost till daylight.

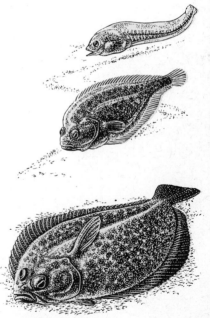

MIGRATING EYE of a flatfish, normal in the larval stage (*top*), begins to move, left or right according to species, as the fish grows (*center*) and winds up next to the other eye (*bottom*). Only one eye travels.

Investigators guessed that the strange echoes must come from some form of life, but they could not be sure because an echo sounder does not put out the right kind of sound waves to pick up echoes from every kind of life. It can get echoes only from objects of a specific size and structure—and these will vary with the wave length of the sound being sent out. J. B. Hersey and others at Woods Hole have made some inroads on this problem by setting off small charges of TNT under water. The sound waves from these explosions produce a variety of echoes from many kinds of fish. "Imagine somebody thumping a bag of sand in the sea," says Hersey, "or hitting a steel ball, or a bell. Each will produce a different sound. It is the same with fish; each produces its own echo, although we don't know yet which fish is which—which is the bag of sand and which the steel ball." Hersey and his associates then proceeded to perfect a combination camera and echo sounder which would take a picture of the specific creature making a specific sound. This technique has helped establish that most of the echoes from the deep scattering layer were reflected from the swim bladders of enormous quantities of small fish from one to six inches long. The reason that the scattering layer rises in the sea at night is that the water cools off, and the plankton, which has gone deep during the day to avoid the heat of the sun, heads for the surface after sundown, and the echo-producing fish follow it up.

Other migratory movements of fish are also determined by where food is to be found or by spawning needs. Bluefin tuna follow a regular migration route, only part of which is now known. They spawn somewhere south of the Bahamas and arrive in the Gulf Stream in May thin and hungry, weighing about 400 pounds apiece. Eating as they go, they reach Nova Scotia in September, by which time they weigh 700 pounds. This phenomenal growth has been verified by catching the same fish twice, first in the Bahamas, where it is weighed and tagged, then in the North Atlantic, where it is weighed again. Similarly, Pacific salmon migrate from their ocean ranges to the headwaters of Oregon and Washington rivers to spawn and die in the exact same pools where they were born.

An even more remarkable migration is that of the eels. Each fall these fish leave European rivers and head across the Atlantic to converge upon a small area in the Sargasso Sea near Bermuda. There they spawn and die. When their eggs hatch, they are caught up by the Gulf Stream and, in a journey that takes three years, float around the great North Atlantic current wheel to the coast of Europe. Developing only then into young elvers, they make their way up river to adult life in fresh waters. Ten years later it is the turn of these fish, having reached the appointed hour in their lives, to head downstream and out through the ocean to the Sargasso Sea. What inborn clock starts them, what inborn compass guides them, remains beyond present understanding.

It is all the more puzzling that other eels which seem identical with the European eels arrive off Bermuda from America to spawn, and in due course their offspring, which appear quite like the European eel larvae, somehow find their way after a mere six months' Gulf Stream trip to American rivers. The migration of the eels remains a most mysterious series of exits and entrances in the great theater of life and death in the sea.

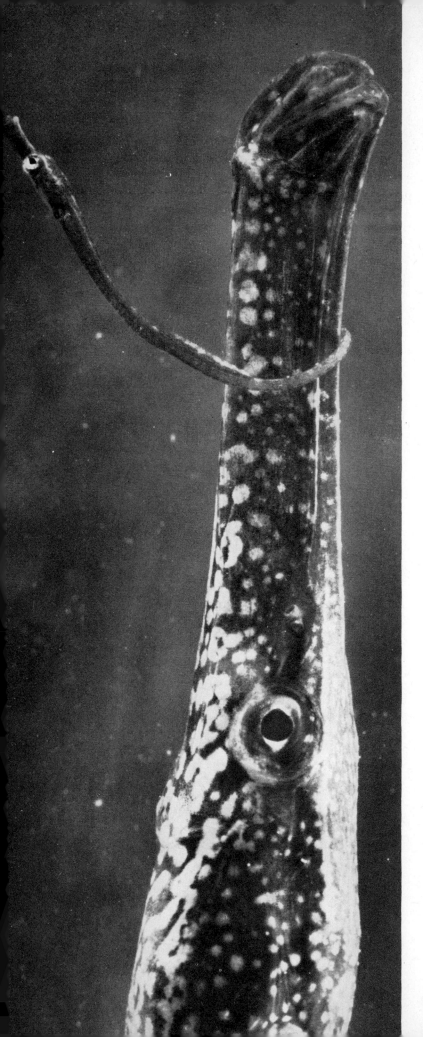

The Skein of Life in the Sea

The skein of life enmeshes every living thing in the sea in an unending struggle for survival. For each plant or animal, the problems of staying alive are the same: getting something to eat and avoiding being eaten. But each solves the problems in a different way. Some solutions and the way they work—and fail—are shown on the following pages.

113

Short Life of a Pipefish

Slim pipefish, which thrive in shallow waters off Sweden's coastline, reverse biological custom in reproduction of their kind. The male pipefish carries the fertilized eggs in a stomach pouch and incubates them for 17 to 21 days before the young fish emerge (*right*). Narrow-leaved eelgrass that grows thickly on the ocean's floor furnishes good camouflaging cover for these poor swimmers (*below*). But the waters throng with foes that eat pipefish (*opposite, bottom*).

A PAIR OF PIPEFISH (*above*) entwine in the weeds. The thin female has deposited her eggs in the male's belly pouch, which now bulges with young.

UNUSUAL BIRTH occurs (*left*) as the baby fish leave a slit in the male's pouch. They are born resembling adults in all but size, which is 20 inches in mature fish.

HUNGRY FRY are never fed by their parents but must start hunting food immediately after birth. At right, several of them are pursuing a school of small shrimps.

SUDDEN DEATH, several hours after its life began, befalls a careless baby pipefish (*below*). Its search for food took it near the tentacles of a hungry jellyfish.

AN UNWARY SWIMMER is eaten by a sea anemone, armed with a battery of tentacles, in the sequence at left. A fish touching the anemone (*top*) is paralyzed by injections from thousands of needles covering each tentacle. The fish is then drawn into the anemone's mouth (*center*) and finally swallowed whole, bulging out the anemone (*bottom*).

STRUGGLING LOBSTER loses a battle with an octopus, which has caught (and immobilized) it in its strong arms, studded with powerful suction discs. After a fight that has roiled the water, the lobster has almost disappeared under the umbrella of tentacles, but its claw shows at right and the fringed segments of its tail are visible in the right fore-ground. The octopus holds the lobster securely with its suckers, tearing out its flesh with a parrotlike beak located on its underside at the center of the circle of tentacles. The octopus and its relatives, the squids, can change color when feeding or alarmed. The tubular opening in the oc-topus' head is the outlet for water pumped over its gills.

SPARKLING DIATOMS, the basic food plants of the sea, are seen here highly magnified. Their tiny bodies, protected by crystal shells, are rich in proteins and vitamins.

STRIPED PORKFISH (*opposite*) swim in schools from Florida to the West Indies. The young fish feed on parasites of larger fish, such as the barracuda and snappers.

Survival by Fertility in the Crowded Sea

Only by reproducing at a tremendous rate do many animal and plant species manage to survive in the sea. The codfish may lay five million eggs in a year and the oyster 500 million. But the best example of survival by fertility is the diatom. This microscopic plant is the meadow grass of the sea, and thousands of kinds of animals, from protozoans to whales, graze its pastures. The diatom reproduces at so rapid a pace that in a month it may have a billion descendants. The chief benefactors of this fecundity are millions of tiny animals the size of amphipods (*next pages*), one of which may eat 100,000 diatoms daily.

Many Legs and Great Agility Spell Safety for Sand Hoppers

Legs are the amphipod's tools for survival. No bigger than a grain of rice, this cousin of the lobster swarms along the East Coast beaches feeding on small plants and animals. Whenever a hungry shore bird or heavy-footed human approaches, it sinks into the sand, digging in with three pairs

of strong, burrowing legs located just under its humped tail (*right*). Much longer, skinnier legs (*extending off the page at right*) are used for crawling. A tangle of appendages toward the amphipod's head are used for swimming and eating. A relative of this amphipod is one of the world's best jumpers. With enormously developed rear legs, it can leap 40 times its own length—the equivalent of a man jumping 240 feet. Normally the burrowing amphipod is colorless. The color seen here is a result of unique polarization methods developed by photomicroscopist Roman Vishniac.

A TRIO OF COLORFUL DAMSELFISH FINDS PROTECTION IN THE LETHAL THICKET FORMED BY THE TENTACLES OF A SOUTH SEA ANEMONE

Marine Arms and Armor

Many marine animals find shelter in small fortresses. Some, like the sea urchin, grow prickly barricades, only to have them demolished by tough-lipped intruders. Others, like the damselfish, live in borrowed battlements. Covered by slime that immobilizes the anemone's stinging mechanism, the damselfish snuggles safely in deadly arms. As if in payment for its haven, it lures other fish into the anemone's reach and has even been seen bringing food morsels to its host.

LACKING IMMUNITY to the anemone's poison, a fish (*left*) lies stung to death in its coils. This anemone's sting cells are located in white bands spiraling around the tentacles.

APPROACHING AN URCHIN, a queen triggerfish assaults the needled armament. The sea urchin is a starfish relative, but it has very long spines which are sometimes poisonous.

DEMOLISHING ITS PREY (*right*) the fish nips off the spines, exposing the fleshy interior of the urchin. The triggerfish is equipped for the job with 14 teeth and tough skin.

SCAVENGING CRUMBS after the queen triggerfish has eaten all that it wants, smaller fish gather around the pile of spines to eat any shred of urchin that might be left behind.

Survival by Disguise

Camouflage is a vital art in the sea. The most common example is that of the fish that are bluish on top but have silvery bellies. Enemies above them find it hard to distinguish blue backs from the surrounding water. From underneath, the light undersides blend into the bright sky. Other fish use more exotic forms of camouflage, not only for defense but to fool and trap their prey (*next pages*).

HALF BURIED, a sting ray (*below*) is nearly invisible. A bottom feeder, it protects itself with a poisonous barbed tail.

A MOCK EYE (*above*) adorns the tail of the butterfly fish. A foe striking at this "eye" meets empty water as the fish darts ahead.

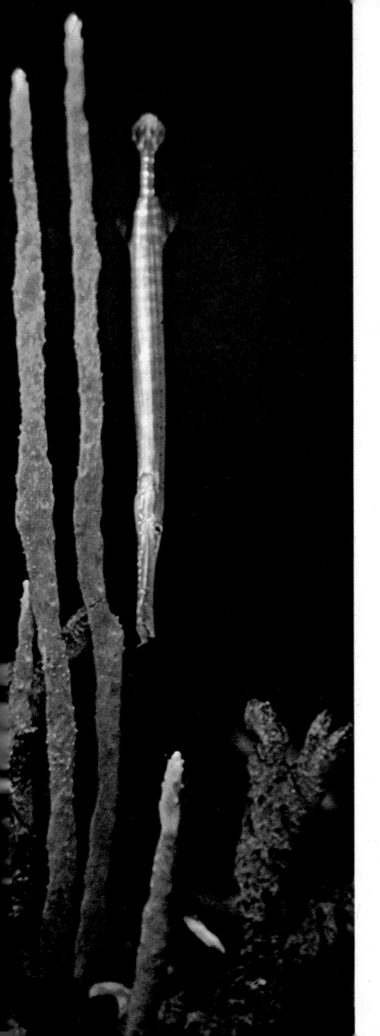

A MARINE CHAMELEON, the yellow-fin grouper is usually a dark color (*top*), but when it is alarmed it changes color to blend with its surroundings (*bottom*).

A FALSE SPIRE of sponge is formed by a slender trumpet fish (*left*) as it hovers motionlessly the instant danger nears. The fish often eats in this headstand position.

A FROGFISH, festooned with filaments of skin, simulates an algae-covered rock. Only its blue eyes betray it. The knot of flesh hanging from its forehead acts as a lure. When an unwary fish investigates too closely, it is sucked into a cavernous mouth. The delicately colored strands in the background are the tentacles of marine worms.

A SARGASSUM FISH not only takes on the color of the sargassum weed in which it lives but is also covered with tassels and ribbons which imitate the plant's air-filled flotation bladders. Although this fish is only an inch long, it is a greedy flesh eater. When not swimming, it climbs among the sargassum with handlike fins, hunting for food.

THIRTY-TWO BLUE EYES RING THE SHELL OF THE COMMON SCALLOP. THEY ARE VERY SIMILAR IN BASIC STRUCTURE TO HUMAN EYES

The Five Senses Guide Sea Animals in Survival

Animal survival depends upon efficient response to danger or opportunity, and the five familiar senses of sight, taste, smell, touch and hearing are vital to sea animals. Arthropods, fish and some mollusks have sharp eyes, although most marine animals are probably nearsighted since visibility is limited even in clear water. The simple jellyfish may be able only to tell light from dark. Taste and smell are most likely combined into a single sense underwater, the sea odors becoming water-borne flavors. Touch occurs in most animals; even the lowly anemone reacts instantly when a tentacle is grazed. Scientists say that hearing is also well developed in the sea. Skin divers say they hear whistles, grunts and clicks in the so-called silent depths.

THE FILE SHELL (*above*) has smaller eyes than the common scallop (*left*) but more prominent tentacles, its organs of taste and smell. Its tentacles also paddle a current of plankton-laden water through its tubular nest, built of fibers which it secretes.

THE OCTOPUS EYE (*right*) is physically like the human eye, and is part of the most highly evolved nervous system found in lower animals. Similarity of eyes does not indicate that man and octopus are closely related, but rather means that each developed the organ independently. This phenomenon is called convergent evolution.

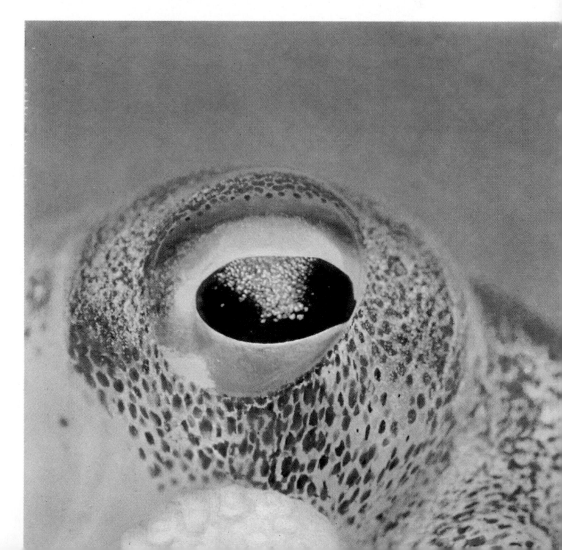

7

FEARSOME FACE of a
sand tiger shark masks
a sluggish nature. Numerous
rows of jagged teeth are
shed and replaced, row
by row. Growing to 10 feet
and weighing up to 300 pounds,
it sometimes attacks men.

Sharks and Other Killers

On a warm day in May 1959, Albert Kogler and Shirley O'Neill, both 18 and students at San Francisco State College, decided to cool off with a swim in the Pacific. Splashing into the surf at Bakers Beach just outside San Francisco's Golden Gate, they swam seaward some 50 yards, Kogler in the lead. "I heard him scream," Miss O'Neill said later. "I turned around and saw this big gray thing flap up into the air. There was a threshing in the water. He screamed again. 'It's a shark—get out of here!'"

Above the scene on the cliff-top grounds of the Presidio, the United States Army post overlooking Golden Gate, Master Sergeant Leo P. Day watched the struggle with the shark. "I could see the boy in the foaming red water, shouting and signaling someone to go back, go back. Then I saw the girl, swimming toward him with frantic strokes, completely ignoring his warning."

Miss O'Neill reached for Kogler's hand. "But when I pulled I could see his arm was just hanging by a thread." So she put her arm about Kogler's back and started for shore. She dragged him close enough for a fisherman to throw a line and pull them the rest of the way.

His body half drained of blood, the boy died two and a half hours later. From the teeth marks, experts identified the attacker as a great white shark. For what Sergeant Day called "the greatest exhibition of courage I have ever seen," President Kennedy in 1961 awarded Miss O'Neill the Young American Medal for Bravery.

NINE RULES TO LESSEN DANGER FROM SHARKS

■ Don't swim or skin dive without a companion.

■ Don't swim at night, or in very murky water.

■ Don't stay in water with a bleeding wound.

■ Don't panic or thrash after sighting a shark. Swim away smoothly to a boat or beach.

■ If a shark moves in, hit it on the snout with a heavy object. Don't use your fist. Rough hide will only cut your skin, making you bleed.

■ Don't tow speared fish at your belt. Boat them immediately.

■ Don't ever tease or spear a shark, no matter how small or harmless it may seem.

■ Don't trail arms or legs from an air mattress or life raft.

■ If you have clothes on, don't take them off. They protect you from shark-skin lacerations.

Facing a shark always takes courage. Consciously or unconsciously, men are afraid of sharks, perhaps because they are just about the only creatures left in nature that will attack men without provocation. In World War II a training manual which the United States Navy issued to men serving in shark-infested areas played down the menace of the shark. An article in a national magazine debunked the shark and portrayed it as cowardly —easy to scare off with a shout or a swat on the snout. This notion is false.

Quite apart from all the hairbreadth escapes told and retold around the beaches of the world, sharks each year make at least several dozen proved attacks on human beings that end in death or maiming. In one place alone —the waters along Australia's east coast—more than 200 authenticated shark attacks on human beings have been recorded in 150 years. In 1959, the last year for which figures are available, 36 proved attacks took place around the world, 13 of which resulted in death. Of the 36 attacks, 10 occurred in United States waters; three were fatal. Like young Kogler, the victims died deaths of horror, often dismembered bite by bite.

In fearful and wonderful ways sharks combine primitiveness and superb adaptability. Unlike the bony fish, which developed much later, sharks have skeletons of cartilage. Three immense fore-and-aft groups of muscles provide most of their motive power. Their brains are tiny—seldom over three inches long even in large sharks. In contrast with bony fish, which strew their eggs carelessly about the sea, most sharks give birth to live young. The young emerge six to 60 at a time after having reached a length of as much as 18 inches, and are able to swim and fend for themselves.

Lacking the swim bladders found in bony fish, sharks must keep moving to stay up, and have taller tails and broader fins than most other varieties. When sharks die they sink like stones. But they are so durable that it often seems they will never die. Whalers tell of sharks that have been caught, disemboweled and thrown into the water, only to swim straight to whales tied alongside the ship and begin tearing at the flesh. Sharks have wreaked havoc in boats after being hooked, harpooned and shot full of lead. In one case on record the severed head of a shark bit off a sailor's finger.

Sharks seem remarkably insensitive to pain, but this does not mean that they lack highly developed senses. They are equipped with the keenest olfactory receptors and can detect blood or a dying fish hundreds of yards away in the water. They have earned the nickname "swimming nose." Experts have long thought that sharks' eyesight is poor and that they do not depend on it. But Perry W. Gilbert of Cornell University recently put blinders on captive sharks at the American Museum of Natural History's Lerner Marine Laboratory in the Bahamas and watched the sharks crash head-on again and again into walls before learning to navigate by feel of fin.

From snout to tail the shark's body resembles a rasp. It is covered with thousands of tiny sharp protuberances called placoid scales. They are rough enough to make the slap of a big shark's tail almost as deadly as its bite. Sharks may bump before biting, giving swimmers a glancing swipe that will shred the skin or slash a rubber life raft.

As far as teeth are concerned, the shark is superbly equipped. Its mouth is literally studded with several sets of needle-sharp teeth, one row in back of another, loosely set in the jaw so that when the front ones break off or wear out there are spares that work their way forward to replace them. Shark bites have an unmistakable crescent shape and are often so deep that a major artery is severed. Many victims die from loss of blood before they can be got ashore.

Despite their reputation for ferocity, sharks are undiscriminating scavengers. They will swallow anything: sea turtles, sea lions, birds, fish, lobsters, horseshoe crabs, garbage, coal, people. One shark captured off an Australian dock had in its stomach half a ham, several legs of mutton, the hindquarters of a pig, the head and forelegs of a bulldog with a rope tied around its neck, a quantity of horseflesh, a piece of cloth and a ship's scraper. Another, caught in the Adriatic, had an even more bizarre bellyful: three overcoats, a nylon raincoat and an automobile license plate.

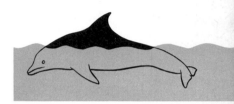

Sharks just bite and swallow, and apparently some can store food in their bellies for days or weeks without digesting it. It was this outlandish ability, as shown by a captive shark, that led to the sensational affair celebrated in Australia as the Shark Arm Murder Case.

In 1935 a big tiger shark was caught and installed as a featured attraction at a Sydney aquarium. Eight days later the shark suddenly disgorged a human arm—so well preserved that medical examiners could make out an identifying tattoo on it. They could also see that the arm had been separated from its owner by a knife and not by the shark's teeth. Following up these leads, the police traced the arm to an amateur boxer who had disappeared two weeks before. Police deduced that the boxer had been done in by fellow conspirators when their scheme for wrecking a yacht to collect insurance had gone awry. The suspected murderers evidently had managed to jam most of the body into a box and drop it overboard, but the arm would not fit in. The shark got—and preserved—the evidence.

Not all of the 250 known species of shark are equally dangerous to man. Some are only a foot long. Others, like the dogfish common in East Coast waters of the United States, have never been known to bother swimmers. Two species—the basking shark and the whale shark—are harmless although they reach a length of 30 to 60 feet and are the largest of all fish, the largest creatures in the sea except for whales. They are plankton feeders, unequipped to attack man. The true killers, experts consider, belong to 30 species ranging in size from five to 25 feet.

EVIL-LOOKING FIN is not necessarily that of a shark (*top*). The porpoise (*second*) has a similar dorsal fin but it shows its back as it rolls in the water. The swordfish (*third*) shows its tail. The manta (*bottom*) shows two parallel wing tips.

Much the most dangerous is the great white shark, a fast-moving, powerfully muscled brute that sometimes weighs nearly four tons. Great whites, according to one English writer, have "a vast greediness after human flesh." They have attacked American bathers as far north as Cape Cod along the Atlantic Coast.

Closely related to the great white, and an even faster swimmer, is the mako shark, a deep-water species much hunted by game fishermen because of the spectacular leaping fight it puts on when hooked. Another fierce variety, the hammerhead, has a weird T-shaped head that looks like a hammer, which it apparently uses as a kind of rudder for rapid turning. At least two of the proved 1959 attacks in United States waters can be blamed on hammerheads. They are bottom feeders given to lurking close inshore and along coral reefs. Spearfishermen should avoid carrying speared and bleeding fish at their belts in areas that hammerheads and other dangerous sharks are known to infest.

The largest group of man-killers is the requiem sharks; nobody knows how they got this grimly appropriate name. By far the most common of the group is the tiger shark, a striped species feared equally in the West Indies and Australia. Also common is the lemon shark, a smaller scavenger whose digestive fluid, dropped on a man's hand, is said to be powerful enough to burn the skin. No one, to date, has tested this bit of folklore, and it is probably no more true than the idea that a shark has to roll over on its side in order to bite. Some sharks do this, but they do not have to. The lemon shark has a yellowish belly. Like the tiger shark, it is often seen skulking around docks and anchored ships, wolfing up offal thrown into the water. Out at sea the best-known of the requiem family are the blue and white-tipped sharks.

Sharks occur in nearly all latitudes; there is even an Arctic species, the Greenland shark. However, the vast majority of sharks are found in temperate and tropical seas, and nearly all shark attacks on humans have taken place when the water temperature has been over 70 degrees Fahrenheit. It has been argued that it is only when the water is warm that people go swimming, but recent studies indicate there is more to it than this: shark appetites seem to go up and down with the water temperature.

Sharks have been known to forage far up rivers. They have attacked Indian pilgrims in the Ganges, and bitten men, women and children in an Iranian river 90 miles from the sea. One casualty of an Iranian attack was a British ambulance driver who had driven his ambulance into the water to wash it. He was standing in a foot of water when struck; he nearly lost a leg. Another species, a grey man-eater that grows to a length of eight to 10 feet, has established itself in the fresh waters of Central America's Lake Nicaragua, probably after migration upriver long ago from the Caribbean, and has killed a number of bathers.

No one really knows what makes one shark rip a man, another circle uncertainly and another turn indifferently away. After more than a hundred undersea shark encounters, Jacques-Yves Cousteau, author of *The Silent World*, the skin diver's bible, limits himself to two conclusions: "The better acquainted we become with sharks, the less we know them; and one can never tell what a shark is going to do." V. M. Coppleson of Australia, one of the world's leading authorities on shark attack, believes that once sharks have tasted human flesh they may acquire the appetite for it.

Some sharks also seem to have the curious trait of picking out a single

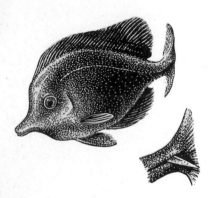

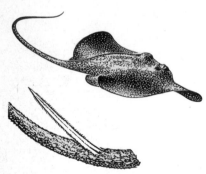

BIZARRE WEAPONS give names to the fish on these pages. The yellow surgeon (*top*) has bony "knives" that flash from grooves in its body when it is molested. The sting ray, which lies on the sea floor, injects venom with a lash of its barbed tail when it is stepped on.

person in a group and limiting their attacks to him. A gruesome example of this behavior occurred on the California coast in 1952 when a 17-year-old boy was attacked by a shark several hundred yards offshore. Five men swam to the boy's aid. They put him on an inflated tire tube and started to push him to shore. As they swam, the shark circled, then slipped through to bite the injured boy again, this time fatally.

Over the years, amateurs and experts alike have proposed all sorts of schemes and devices for ending the shark menace: mechanical noise-makers to scare the sharks away, electrified barriers and air-bubble curtains to fence them off, and hunter-killer task forces of planes and surface craft to exterminate them. In the end the most effective device found for protecting beaches in shark-infested areas is what Australians call "meshing." The technique is to place loosely hanging nets in the water overnight around the bathing beaches. These are designed to entangle sharks and thus reduce the shark population. First tried at Sydney's big beaches in 1937, the nets caught 1,500 sharks, 900 of them probably man-eaters, in just over a year. Since then the catch has dropped to 200 a year, and the number of attacks on bathers at meshed beaches has fallen to zero.

For a sailor on a life raft or a skin diver on a tropical reef, there is Shark Chaser, a shark repellent developed for the Navy in World War II. Shark Chaser contains copper acetate, a chemical supposed to be unpleasant to sharks, but there is little evidence that it is effective. During tests near Brisbane, Australia, sharks kept gobbling up packets of shark repellent as it was thrown in the water. A more effective second ingredient in Shark Chaser is a dye called nigrosine. This spreads a blue-black cloud in the water that has kept single sharks from closing in on swimmers.

Neither Shark Chaser nor anything else has proved effective when sharks go on a mass rampage known as a "feeding frenzy." This may occur when bait or entrails are dumped overboard from a fishing boat, attracting sharks in droves. Then the sea churns with fins and foam as the sharks, crazed by the blood in the water, slash at anything, often biting chunks out of each other. Men in the water are helpless during a feeding frenzy. One of the worst mass shark attacks on record took place in 1942 when the troopship *Nova Scotia* was torpedoed at night off the coast of South Africa. A thousand men were lost, many of them presumably to the sharks. The next morning numerous legless bodies were found floating in the water.

Of all the large creatures in the sea, only the shark is a real menace to man. The giant squid, although it looks fearsome enough and is the prototype for many a sea-monster legend, lives at depths and distances remote from man and never bothers him at all. Another creature that looks as if it should be a menace, but is not, is the giant devilfish, or manta ray. Like nearly all the biggest whales and sharks, the manta feeds placidly on plankton. Though it casts a terrifying shadow when it floats over a skin diver's head, and makes a terrifying splash when it leaps and lands on the water's surface, the worst this 3,500-pound giant of the rays will do to man is accidentally tangle up a diver's air hose.

Aside from the shark, the most dangerous salt-water fish is probably the great barracuda. Sleek, cigar-shaped, four to six feet long, this species is feared by many Florida and West Indian divers more than the shark. This

SWORD AND BLUDGEON are the weapons of the great fish above. The swordfish (*top*) slashes through schools of fish, killing, maiming and impaling. Circling back, it eats at leisure. The sawfish flails its prey with its serrated snout, and also uses it to probe sandy bottoms for food.

is partly because barracuda outnumber sharks in those warm, reef-studded waters, partly because even when not intending to attack a swimmer they have the unnerving habit of inquisitively following him around. Their eyesight is sharp and they are attracted by bright, flashing objects, by legs dangling from rafts, even by waders along the beach. When a barracuda strikes, it leaves a clean, straight-line wound, utterly unlike the ragged tear left by a shark. Since 1884, there have been 14 attacks that can be charged with certainty to the great barracuda. Others have probably been attributed erroneously to sharks. Still others have probably resulted in the death by drowning, or by loss of blood, of swimmers in remote West Indian islands, and have thus gone unrecorded. In general, however, the attack of a barracuda is much less likely to be fatal than that of a shark because the barracuda does not return to attack. It strikes once and is gone.

Moray eels, the fierce-looking, thickset creatures of tropical reefs, are dangerous to man in only one respect. A diver who pokes a hand into a hole occupied by a moray eel may get bitten. Furthermore the eels are strong and they will not let go, and a man engaged with a moray runs a chance of drowning before he can pry himself loose. But this action is purely defensive; morays cannot be considered a menace to man.

Of the mammals of the sea, two are known to be real killers. Luckily man rarely runs into either of them. The sea leopard, a 12-foot-long Antarctic seal that preys on lesser seals, has a well-authenticated taste for warm-blooded animals. One of these animals nearly caught a member of the Shackleton Antarctic Expedition of 1914-1916. First it floundered across the floes after him, then dived into the water and swam under the ice, following him by his shadow, and burst out again in front of him as he ran. The explorer's life was saved only when another member of the party heard him yelling, ran up and shot the sea leopard.

The other warm-blooded potential man-eater is the 30-foot killer whale. This rapacious beast ranges in all seas, particularly in the higher latitudes, hunting in packs of a few up to 40 individuals, devouring penguins, fish, walruses and seals. It has a particular fondness for the tongues of larger whales. Like dolphins or porpoises, killer whales are reputed to be very intelligent. Tasmanian coastal whalers claim that occasionally a pack of killers will herd small whales toward their waiting boats, probably just to get the tongues.

Though no proved killer-whale attacks on humans have been reported, men who live by the sea in small boats are afraid of them, or so reports Gavin Maxwell about Scottish fishermen. Others point out that lone Eskimo hunters may well have been picked off many times, with no surviving witness. Polar explorers have observed how killer whales may do this— by bumping up under ice floes to spill their prey into the sea. On a recent Antarctic expedition a United States Navy photographer decided to test this when the presence of killer whales was heralded by a horde of penguins and seals leaping out of the water and onto the ice to avoid being eaten. The photographer and his companions began jumping up and down on the ice to attract the whales, and the whales responded by bumping from below. But when one actually poked its head out of the water for a portrait, the ice began to crack and the men sensibly fled.

Man Against Shark

PROTECTED BY STEEL BARS, A PHOTOGRAPHER DESCENDS INTO SHARK-PATROLLED WATERS

In speed, power and appetite, the shark is a formidable ocean predator. The little we know of this dangerous, unpredictable fish has been learned at a high cost in human life. But today scientists in protective cages are studying the shark in its home waters. And skilled divers are testing it in combat—and living to tell the tale.

FATALLY SPEARED, a hammerhead thrashes the water in its death throes. It is a powerful fish and if hooked on a line it has been known to fight until dead of exhaustion.

CLOSE TO DEATH, the hammerhead is so weak that the hunter can approach it. The small fish are remora, which attach themselves to the shark with strong sucker discs.

Hammerheaded Adversary

Few sights are more terrifying for a skin diver than the ugly form of an approaching hammerhead shark. The animal comes out of the murk like some prehistoric monster, zeroing in on its victim. Eyes at the tips of its grotesque head lobes enable it to see backward as well as forward. Using these fleshy projections for balance, it hangs motionless before it makes its attack. Unless the diver is a skilled spear hunter, like the one opposite, he may go down on a long list as another victim of the hammerhead, one of the most notorious man-killers of all the sharks.

ATTRACTED BY BLOOD from a speared hogfish, a 12-foot hammerhead menaces a careless fisherman in tropical waters. Hammerheads are a world-wide danger in warm waters of all oceans and have been seen in fresh-water estuaries. The first fatal shark attack recorded in American waters was by a hammerhead off Long Island in 1815.

Attracted by Blood, Sharks Attack Each Other in Feeding Frenzy

Many of the most vicious sharks live in the open sea. These wanderers include the mako (*leaping, top left*), the white-tipped (*center*) and the blue (*right foreground*). Although these forms normally hunt alone, the smell of

blood is enough to bring them together. Maddened, they go into a so-called "feeding frenzy," in which they slash at anything—including each other. The pack above has disemboweled the blue shark shown with its snout out of the water. In this crazed state they have been known to bite through a wooden keel or chomp down on a whirling propeller. Air or sea disasters in tropical waters have produced feeding frenzies with mass losses of human life.

A HUNGRY KILLER WHALE breaks through Antarctic ice in an effort to eat the man who took this picture. Swift packs of three to 40 killer whales range through all the oceans, eating enormously to nourish huge bodies up to 30 feet in length. In the stomach of one half-grown animal were found the remains of 13 porpoises and 14 seals.

Other Killers of the Sea

The killer whale and the moray eel join the sharks and poison fish in the rogues' gallery of dangerous marine animals. The killer whales are among the largest flesh eaters on earth. They feed mainly on warm-blooded animals and are the most dangerous things a man can meet in the water. Moray eels, some venomous, hide in coral crannies and have earned the name "rattlesnakes of the sea" by snapping at any hand or foot intruding into one of their holes.

A SINUOUS MORAY EEL ventures out of its hole. These are common animals, and dozens, some 10 feet long, may inhabit a small reef. The V-shaped jaws can inflict a jagged wound; worse than this, they may clamp shut till the moray's head is cut off. The eel tolerates the small shrimps clinging to its head because they feed on skin parasites.

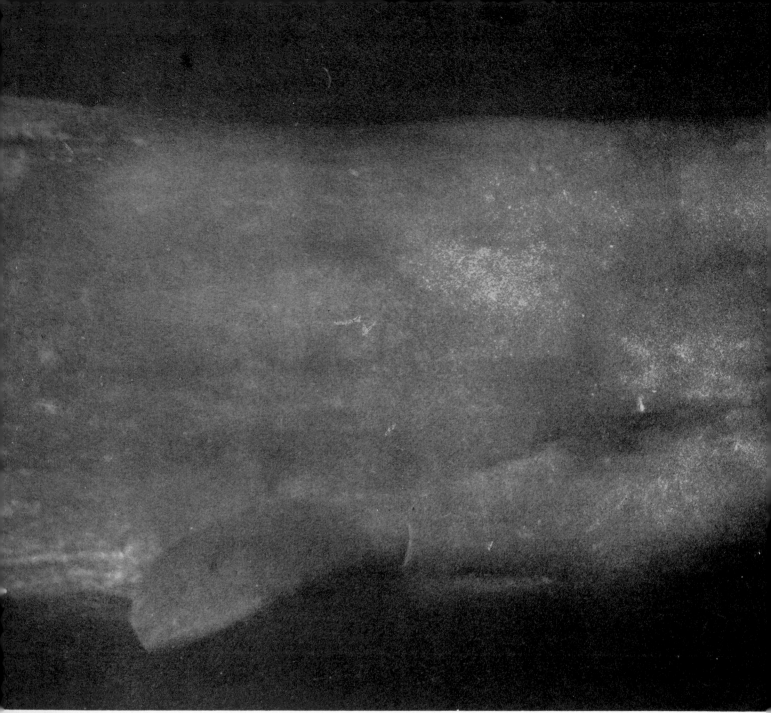

A HUGE SPERM WHALE SHOWS PITTED SCARS OF BATTLES WITH THE GIANT SQUID AS IT SWIMS BY PHOTOGRAPHER HANS HASS.

Mammals of the Sea

8

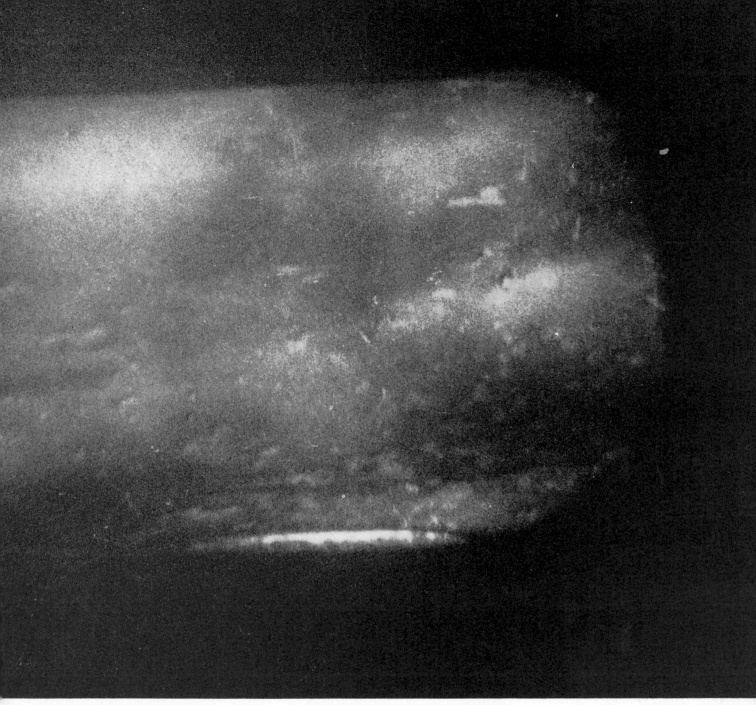

OFF THE AZORES, HASS SCOUTED FOR DAYS IN A SMALL BOAT BEFORE DIVING 45 FEET INTO THE PATH OF AN ONCOMING WHALE

Since there is such an abundance of food in the sea, it is understandable that some of the efficient, highly adaptable, warm-blooded mammals evolved on land should go back there. Those that did have done very well for themselves. Within about 50 million years—no time at all, geologically speaking—one of the four kinds of mammals that have returned to the sea has developed into the largest of all animal forms: the whale. A second kind, the seal, has produced what is probably the greatest population of large carnivorous mammals on earth. This suggests that these top dogs of the ocean heap must be prospering and multiplying nowadays in a style befitting their exalted station. Not so. At least, not for the last 150 years. Trouble has closed in on them in the form of an equally warm-blooded and even more efficient and adaptable predator, man. At sea as on land, man has now planted himself on top of the whole great pyramid of life, and he has been giving the mammals of the sea a very bad time.

There is a simple reason for this. Marine mammals have the misfortune to be swimming aggregates of commodities which man wants: furs, oil, meat. Even so, they might not be so vulnerable to man's depredations if they did not, like man, reproduce so slowly. Every year man takes more than 40 million tons of fish from the oceans without critically depleting the population of any species. The same cannot be said for the slow-breeding mammals of the sea, many of which have been all but stamped out to serve man's wants and whims.

Take the sea otter, a handsome creature, possessing one of the world's most valuable pelts. At the turn of the century the sea otter's sumptuous dark fur commanded prices of $1,700 a skin, and the animal, which had been common from Oregon's Pacific Coast north to Alaska, was hunted to virtual extinction. Laws now protect sea otters. They exist in small numbers in the Aleutian Islands and along the California coast. Of all the warm-blooded creatures that have moved into the sea, sea otters remain closest to the land. They are the only ones that have retained true hind legs. These are short and specialized for swimming, with webbed toes, but they are not flippers. Sea otters are as playful as their slightly smaller fresh-water cousins, the river otters. They have an engaging way of floating on their backs in the ocean, cracking clamshells on rocks held against their chests and lazily stuffing tidbits into their mouths.

Sea cows represent a more pronounced step back to aquatic life than sea otters. These 6-to-10-foot, almost hairless creatures have flippers instead of forelegs, and have lost their hind legs altogether. Their place in the kinship of animals is puzzling, but naturalists think they may be distantly related to elephants. They are another order that has suffered heavily at the hand of man. Some 150 years ago, the bulkiest species, the 30-foot, three-and-a-half ton Steller's sea cow, was wiped out by Bering Sea whalers who hunted it down for its flesh. Two kinds survive: the dugong of the Indian Ocean and the manatee of tropical American and African waters. The female sea cows are the creatures whose habit of standing up in the water and exposing their prominent breasts is supposed to have incited early sailors to babbling about mermaids. Actually manatees are bald, harelipped, mustached, thick-necked animals. They lounge sluggishly about river mouths and along coasts and feed on vegetation. They breed and bear their young at sea, and are very awkward and almost helpless out of water.

What is believed to be the largest surviving group of big carnivorous mammals in the world today consists of about 25 million individual fin-footed animals of 47 species divided into three groups—the eared seals, the true seals and the walruses. Eared seals, which include sea lions and fur seals, still have external ears; the true seals and walruses have lost these impediments to swift underwater swimming and in general have moved closer to the streamlined fish shape.

Fur seals were butchered in the north for 200 years. In the Pribilof Islands the population was reduced from more than two million to scarcely more than a hundred thousand by the turn of the century. Since 1911 the United States has administered an international agreement to protect the Pribilof herds. The effect on the seals has been electric; their numbers are now back to about two million. A sadder story is that of the walrus. Like its smaller cousin the fur seal, the one-and-a-half ton walrus was once abundant throughout the Arctic. But hunters pursued it relentlessly because, in addition to its hide and oil, its two-foot tusks fetched a good price in the ivory market. The cruelest stratagem was to catch a walrus calf and beat it until it cried. Since walruses are devoted parents, every adult within hearing would rush to the calf's aid—and into the butchers' trap. Today the only walruses left roam a few remote areas of Greenland and the Arctic.

Sea lions have escaped such destruction largely because they never had as great commercial value. One variety is the so-called trained seal of the circus; even without man's prompting, it likes to toss and catch fish as it sports off its native Pacific rocks. Bull sea lions, which are twice as big as the cows, collect harems of up to 20 cows when the breeding season starts and do their best to act like lords of creation. Bull fights bull for harem rights; the losing bulls—the old, the young, the weak—are either killed or flop disconsolately off to bachelor quarters.

True seals range more widely than the eared varieties and one of them, the monk seal, so far departs from the normal cold-water haunts of seals as to live in the tropics. The largest true seals are the sea elephants, which grow to 16 feet in length and 12 feet in girth and have an odd, 15-inch "trunk" hanging down over their noses. Almost exterminated for their blubber, sea elephants are making a comeback in the Antarctic and on Guadalupe Island off Lower California.

Of the warm-blooded animals that have returned to the sea, none has made the transition so completely as the whale—and none has been more remorselessly slaughtered by man. From early times men felt magic in the mighty leviathan. Even now, when modern men and their machines have driven most of the big whales to a last Antarctic stronghold, it is impossible for most of us to look upon these wonderful animals with anything but fascination and awe.

Not all whales are big, of course; some are no more than four and a half feet long. Of the hundred-odd species, almost half are dolphins and porpoises. The order is divided into two groups—baleen whales and toothed whales. Baleen whales, which are the biggest of them all, have what amounts to huge strainers of a tough and flexible stuff called whalebone, or baleen, inside their mouths. The whales with teeth include not only the broad-domed, 60-foot-long sperm whale—Captain Ahab's foe in *Moby Dick*—but the killer whale and all the other dolphins and porpoises as well.

The whale is so well adapted to the realm of the sea that many people still think of it as a fish. It has no need, as some other warm-blooded marine animals do, to go on land to bear its young. It is marvelously streamlined. Its neck bones have shortened to merge the massive head with the trunk. Its forelegs have become stabilizing fins and its hind legs have completely disappeared. The only remains of its external ear are openings on either side of the head just large enough to pass a pencil through. The nostrils have moved from the front to the very top of the head and have

SKELETONS of porpoise (*top*) and sea lion (*bottom*) show vestiges of earlier land adaptation. The porpoise had five digits but has lost one in aquatic adaptation. The sea lion has kept five digits, and hind legs, which the porpoise has lost. For strength in swimming, the porpoise has a thicker backbone.

become one or two blowholes which enable the whale to breathe without raising itself more than a few inches above the water's surface. A thick layer of blubber not only conserves body heat in cold polar seas but further improves streamlining and acts as a food reserve when the whale travels to warmer waters where its kind of food is not abundant.

The biggest whales are bigger than any land animal could be. The largest ever caught was a female blue that measured 113.5 feet. It used to be thought that whales weighed about a ton a foot. But British scientists have weighed three large whales piece by piece (there is no way of weighing a sizable whale all at once) and found that big ones work out to a ton and a half per foot. This means that the record blue probably weighed 170 tons, as much as 2,267 150-pound human beings.

A whale can grow to such size because water supports its weight against the pull of gravity. When the linear dimensions of an animal are doubled, its volume, and therefore its weight, will increase no less than eightfold. This means that a land animal's legs must be eight times stronger to support only a twofold increase in size. For the whale, freed by the sea from gravity's heaviest shackles, great size actually increases efficiency. Great size means vastly greater volume, and hence much more room for muscles, to generate the swimming power needed to overcome the water's frictional drag. The entire rear third of the whale is an engine of enormous muscles. These enable the whale's 12-foot tail flukes to execute a semirotary sculling motion that works with the same effect as a ship's propeller, generating as much as 520 horsepower in a 90-footer, according to the estimate of one scientist. Large blue whales can make 20 knots when pressed, and can run all day ahead of a whaling ship making 10 knots.

All big whales except the sperm whale are baleen whales. They feed on krill and other small creatures of the sea by swimming along at slow speed with their mouths open. Their jaws are so wide that a tremendous volume of water pours in and is then forced out at the sides through baleen strainers which hang down on each side of the mouth like a curtain. Great numbers of krill and other tiny marine animals are caught in the baleen as the water passes through. Every now and then the whale's tongue wipes the baleen clean and passes the food back to its gullet.

Many whales pass about six months of the year in polar waters where plankton is the richest, and then travel to tropical seas to breed and bear young, undoubtedly so that their babies will have warm water to swim in until they grow a protective coat of blubber. Baleen whales are believed to pair off during each breeding season. Bull sperm whales are like bull seals: they collect harems.

The female blue whale generally gives birth to a single calf every other year. Female blues are somewhat bigger than their mates, and their calves are astonishingly big—23 feet at birth in the case of a typical blue-whale calf, or almost a third the size of its mother. For seven months the female blue supplies its baby with a ton of very rich milk a day, according to one estimate, while lying still on the surface of the sea. By the time the blue calf is weaned it is already more than 50 feet long, as long as full-grown whales of many species, and by the time it is two years old it may already have attained a length of 75 feet. The blue whale and its more common

FOOD STRAINERS called baleen grow in the right whale's mouth. The whale swims with jaws wide open (*top*) into masses of plankton. The water goes through the curtain of baleen and is forced out of the sides of the whale's mouth by the tongue, but the plankton is left, to be licked back into the gullet. The lower drawing shows how the baleen is set in relation to the whale's skull and jaw.

Antarctic cousin, the fin whale, reach sexual maturity in four or five years, but they keep on growing until they are about twelve. Studying wax plugs laid down in year-by-year layers inside whales' ear membranes, scientists believe that blue whales live at least 50 years.

The sperm whale, whose oil provided the wealth of New England's great 19th Century whaling industry, is in many respects the most interesting of all whales. It is the only big whale with teeth, which are peglike and about eight inches long. They are all in the lower jaw, and they fit into holes in the leathery upper jaw when the long narrow mouth is snapped shut. The sperm whale needs its teeth to fight and kill its favorite food, the giant squid. It dives down more than half a mile to feed, nosing in the deep and along the bottom for squid and octopus, sometimes staying there for 40 minutes before coming up to blow. Blowing, or spouting, is simply the exhaling of a whale, a great breath of stale air mixed with water vapor ejected into the atmosphere.

The sperm whale gets its name from spermaceti, the oily wax found in an extraordinary storage tank located in its huge square-fronted head. Spermaceti is lighter than water, and it was believed for a long time that the whale's reservoir of this material served as a buoyancy tank. Now it is suspected that it has something to do with the whale's phenomenal ability to dive deep and come up relatively quickly without getting "the bends," the affliction that human divers get when they surface from a dive too fast.

The bends is caused by a sudden release of pressure. Breathing air when exposed to great pressures deep in the water causes nitrogen to be dissolved in a diver's bloodstream. If he surfaces too fast, this dissolved nitrogen will come bubbling out in the blood just like soda gas in a bottle of pop when the cap is removed. These bubbles can clog the veins, damage internal organs, and make the victim writhe in excruciating pain.

Whales do not breathe while underwater, of course. But they do have enormous lungs, and they take in so much air before a dive that deep pressures could theoretically force nitrogen into their blood, and inflict a fatal case of the bends when they tried to come up again. What may prevent this is spermaceti. Waxy or fatty substances can absorb six times as much nitrogen as blood can, and enough spermaceti may get into the whale's respiratory system in the form of a waxy foam so that fabulous half-mile dives can be endured without damage. Proof that sperm whales do dive that deep is provided in a curious way. Every once in a while a drowned whale is found entangled in a transoceanic cable. A cable-repair ship once found one at 3,720 feet.

The sperm whale's predilection for giant squid is the source of one of the ocean's most valuable products. The whale swallows squid whole, but has never been able to digest the hard parrot-like beaks. These sometimes fail to pass through the digestive tract, causing the gradual formation of a dark, sticky material with a foul smell which improves on exposure to the air. This material is ambergris, the best substance known for making perfumes hold their scent. In recent years other perfume fixatives have tended to take its place, but top-grade ambergris is still worth as much as $10 an ounce. Whales frequently succeed in spewing up their ambergris, in which case it may be found floating in the water or washed up on a beach. It is also taken when the whale is cut up.

No one has yet devised an intelligence test for whales. Dolphins, studied in captivity, have shown considerable ability to learn. They are social animals, with a tender regard for their young and a readiness to go to the aid of a fellow, shown for instance when other dolphins try to push a wounded member of their school up for air. Dolphins talk to each other in high, sharp squeaks. They have individual built-in sonar systems, which tell them by the returning echoes of their chirps where to locate prey. Whales also travel in sociable pods, and evidently have ways of using sound to communicate and locate big shoals of krill. But the whale's intelligence has not been strong enough to enable it to cope with its one great enemy, man. In the past two and a half centuries, man has hunted down and slaughtered one species of whale after another.

The first species brought near to extinction was the Atlantic right whale. Whalers of the 17th Century called this black, oil-rich 60-footer a "right" whale because it floated when killed; most other whales were "wrong" because they sank when killed and were lost. The Atlantic right whale was almost gone by the end of the 17th Century, whereupon whalers next gave chase to the bowhead or Greenland or Arctic right whale, whose mouthful of baleen alone, in the years when all fashionable women were corseted in whalebone, could bring $10,000 in world markets. Bowheads were soon all but wiped out.

In the last year of the United States Civil War, a Norwegian whaling-man invented a gun for firing grenade-filled harpoons, and shortly afterward other Norwegians developed power-driven catcher boats and devices for pumping air into captured whales to keep them from sinking. Then for the first time man began to kill the big whales—the blue, the fin, the humpback—that had been "wrong" for earlier whalers. Today the big whales have nearly vanished from the Northern Hemisphere. In the Antarctic, whalers operating giant whaling-factory ships have killed over one million whales in 50 years.

Though international agreements have limited the annual catch since 1932, it has been estimated that the mass-slaughterers of the 20th Century have killed five times as many whales as all the famous whaling fleets of the last century put together. At present, some experts believe there are only 200,000 fin whales left in the Antarctic. How long they can survive is problematical, considering that in the 1958-1959 season alone whalers killed 27,128. For that magnificent animal, the blue whale, the point of no return may already have passed. In spite of the fact that the hunting of blue whales has been severely regulated since 1946, the number seen and caught continues to decline. It may be that blue whales are now so few that they are unable to find mates. Unlike the smaller gray whale, which has been saved from extinction by the fact that the surviving few habitually return to two or three Lower California bays to breed, the blue whale ranges for its feeding and breeding across the whole of the open sea from the Antarctic to the equator. How, in all those vast ocean reaches, are the surviving blue whales to meet others of their kind? Even if the whaling commission should ban all hunting of the blue whale, the next decades may well see the end of the greatest creature ever wrought by nature.

Return to the Sea

FLOATING ON HER BACK, A SEA OTTER CRADLES HER PUP. SHY OF MAN, OTTERS LIVE MAINLY ON SHELLFISH IN COASTAL WATERS

A few mammals that once lived on land have returned to the sea, to continue their evolution there. Some sought food, others fled land enemies. Their names still link them to the land: sea otter, sea lion, sea cow. Almost all have felt the hard hand of man, who has always hunted them for their fur, their flesh and their oil.

BOTTLE-NOSED DOLPHINS (*left*), seeming to grin expectantly, wait for a fish handout at California's Marineland. They reach 12 feet and can swim 22 miles per hour.

THE DUGONG (*above*) weighs 1,000 pounds, may measure 10 feet and feeds on sea plants near the shore. Early Greek sailors thought it a woman, starting the mermaid myth.

Contrasts in Amiability

Both dolphins and dugongs are noted for amiability toward man, but that is their only kinship in behavior. The dolphins, small whales commonly called porpoises, are clever, swift and responsive to training, delighting aquarium visitors with antics that usually draw fish rewards. They have complicated brains comparable to man's, and they learn tricks faster than the brightest primates. They seem to communicate with each other by high-pitched whistles and grunts when feeding, or in moments of distress or pleasure. Some scientists hope eventually to train dolphins to talk.

Dugongs and their close relatives, manatees, are lethargic creatures of little grace that live in shallow coastal waters, where they browse with strong-muscled mouths on sea vegetation. They are easily approached; the dugong of Asiatic shores has been hunted almost to extinction for its oil and its succulent flesh.

153

Seals and Sea Lions

There are about 40 species of seals, living in almost all seas and divided into two categories: eared seals (sea lions and fur seals) and true seals (leopard, ribbon and elephant seals). Eared seals retain two sets of flippers for locomotion on land or ice; true seals, without external ears, have hind flippers fused to their tails and are better adapted to aquatic life. The huge walrus, confined to arctic waters, is a link between the two types. Most seals have been widely hunted for hides, meat, fur and blubber.

BULL ELEPHANT SEAL on subantarctic Kerguelen Island puffs its trunk, ready to fight. Whalers' slaughter of this 16-foot, 5,000-pound seal once brought it near extinction.

GREGARIOUS SEA LIONS (*right*) troop ashore to breed on an Argentine coast. California sea lions are generally used as performing circus seals, being easy to tame and train.

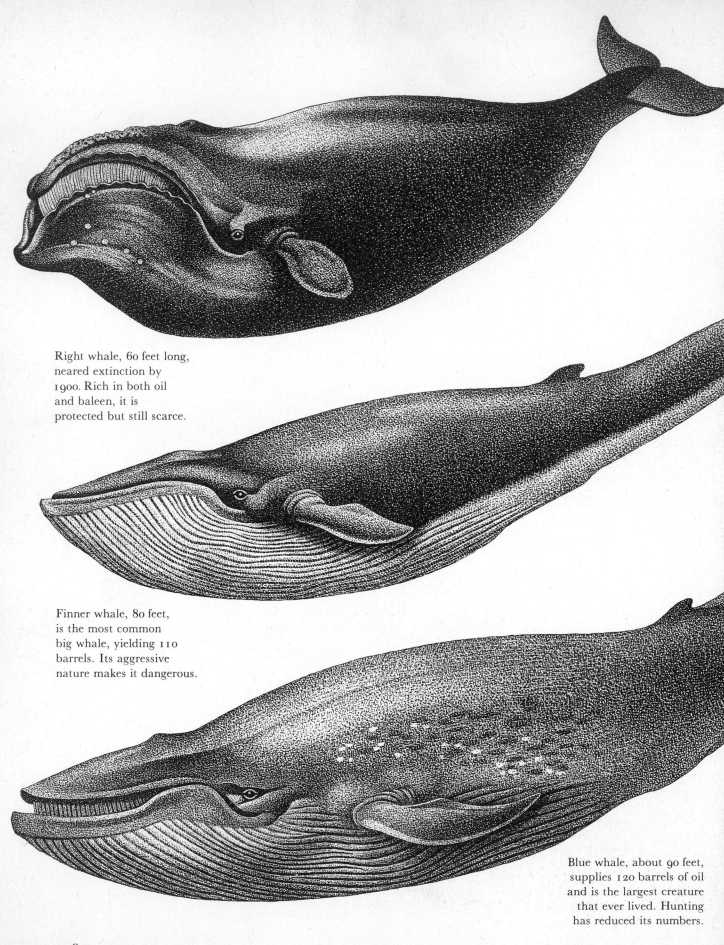

Right whale, 60 feet long,
neared extinction by
1900. Rich in both oil
and baleen, it is
protected but still scarce.

Finner whale, 80 feet,
is the most common
big whale, yielding 110
barrels. Its aggressive
nature makes it dangerous.

Blue whale, about 90 feet,
supplies 120 barrels of oil
and is the largest creature
that ever lived. Hunting
has reduced its numbers.

Five Oil-Bearing Targets for Whalers' Harpoons

The five whales shown here have been among those most hunted by man during 1,000 years of whaling. The right whale is so named because New England whalers said it was the "right" one to kill—its carcass floated, easy to tow and strip at sea. In the 19th Century, Yankee whalers killed an estimated 100,000 right whales. The oil was mainly used for illumination and lubrication; the whalebone gave resilient strength to corsets, buggy whips and umbrellas. Sperm whales were equally prized for their highgrade oil, still valued for precision instruments. This whale is also the world's only source of ambergris, base for expensive perfumes. Modern whalers salvage almost every inch of a kill for use in paint, medicine, cosmetics, soap, human and animal food and fertilizer. Whale oil is used in the manufacture of 50 per cent of Europe's margarine. Japan consumes 100,000 tons of whale meat annually.

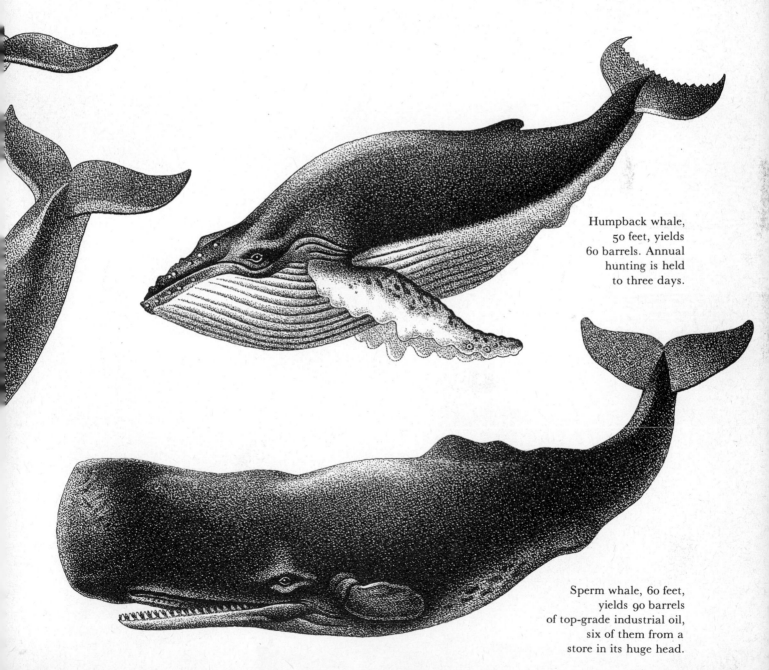

Humpback whale, 50 feet, yields 60 barrels. Annual hunting is held to three days.

Sperm whale, 60 feet, yields 90 barrels of top-grade industrial oil, six of them from a store in its huge head.

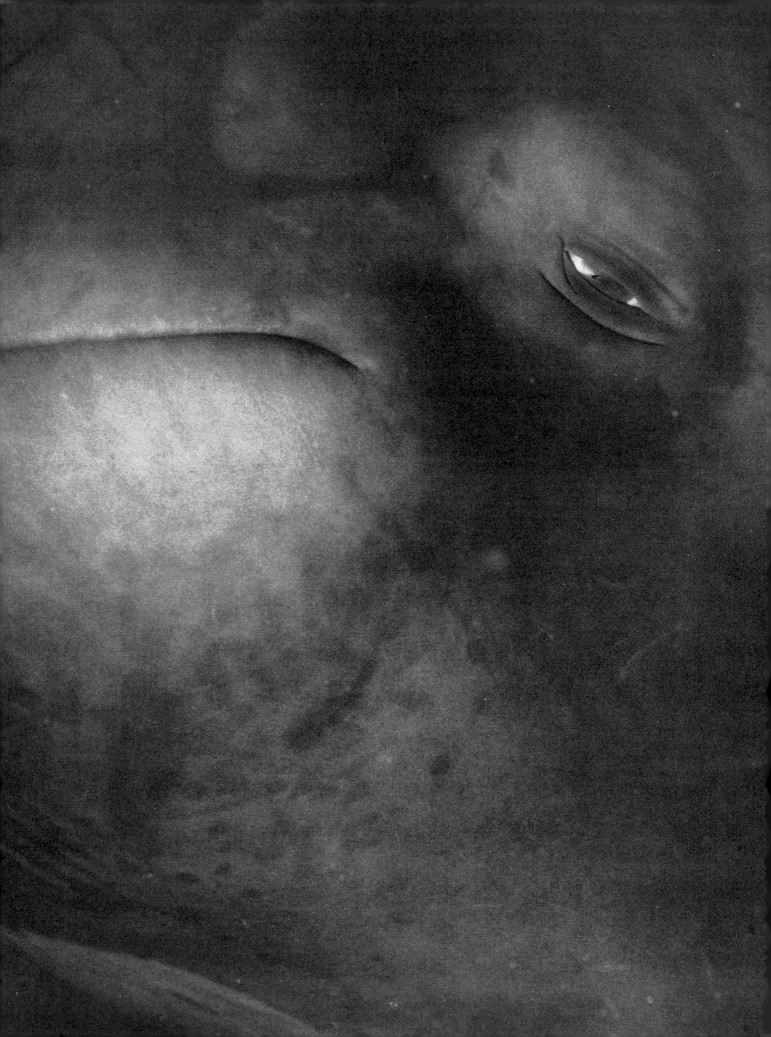

A WHALE'S EYE (*opposite*) has glands that shed grease tears to keep out brine, which is painful to mammals. The whale's vision is not keen. Its sense of smell is also weak. But its hearing, like the bat's, is acute. Some scientists now believe that whales make squeaking sounds in the water and locate objects accurately by the echoes.

GRAY WHALE (*above*) is an Arctic type, averaging 40 feet long, with hair on its head. Fall migrations take it from the Bering Sea to Lower California, where 12-foot calves are born. Estimated at 25,000 in 1840, gray whales were easy prey for whalers, who had killed all but about 100 by the late 1930s. The species' population is now over 5,000.

Modern Harpoon Guns Give Short Shrift to Whales

Today's whaling is a mechanized but bloody business. The whaling fleet, now concentrating mainly in Antarctic waters, consists of small, swift catcher boats and big factory ships. The catcher patrols the sea until it spots a whale, then chases it from sounding to sounding until the whale is too exhausted to dive any more. The catcher approaches within 200 feet and fires an explosive harpoon (*right*). An accurate shot will reach a vital spot for a quick kill. If only wounded, the whale must be played like a fish in a death struggle that may take hours.

A FOUR-FOOT BARBED HARPOON IN ITS BACK, AN 80-FOOT WHALE DYES THE SEA RED WITH ITS BLOOD. BEFORE EXPIRING, ONE

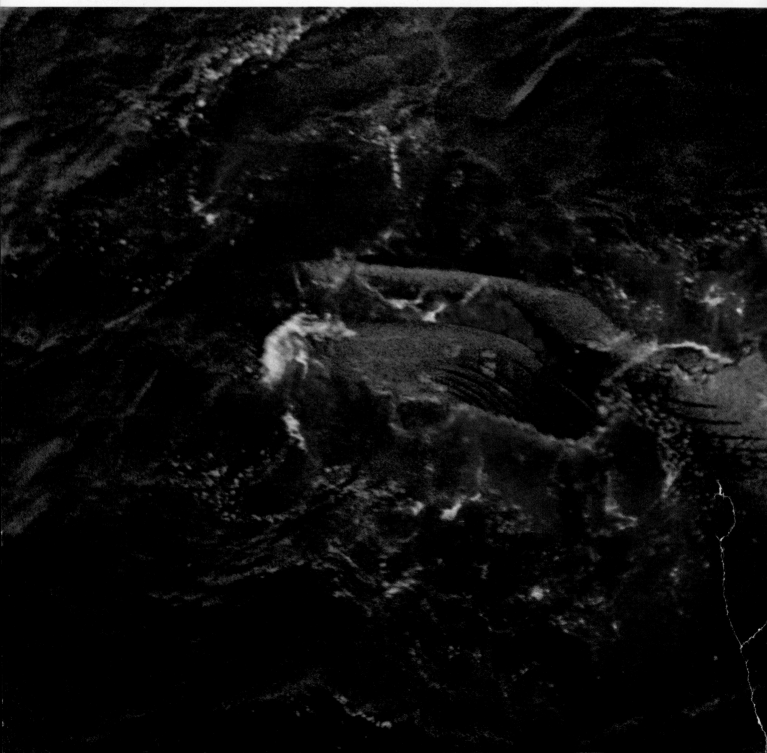

HARPOON GUNNER (*left*) aims his seven-foot gun. The gun was invented by a Norwegian named Svend Foyn. It revolutionized whaling, requiring the use of engine-driven catcher boats as gun platforms and eliminating open whaleboats.

BLUE WHALE TOWED A 90-FOOT CATCHER BOAT (ENGINES FULL SPEED ASTERN) FOR EIGHT AND A HALF HOURS AT FIVE KNOTS

FACTORY SHIP waits for a catcher and its kill at left. It is the mother ship for 11 other catchers, one tanker, and a helicopter used to patrol for whales.

SIX DEAD WHALES lie in the wake of a factory ship as a 190-foot catcher boat edges alongside with another carcass. The bodies are inflated with air to keep them afloat.

A BIG BLUE (*opposite*) is hauled aboard a factory ship. The ramp gets so hot from friction that it must be hosed. The huge balloon (*left foreground*) is inflated mouth tissue.

IN A WHALE'S JAW, men chop at a ton of baleen. Fringed whalebone plates, which strain food from water, distinguish the Mysticeti (baleen) from Odontoceti, which have teeth (*below*).

Butchering a Blue Whale

On a factory ship's deck, steaming with eight tons of blood, a 150-man crew can butcher an 89-foot blue whale, weighing 120 tons, in an hour. Long knives peel off four layers of blubber (26 tons), which are cut into blocks and boiled into oil. On another deck, the meat (56 tons) is separated from the bones (22 tons), which are also rendered. The meat, the internal organs (3.5 tons) and the tongue (3 tons) are processed for human and animal foods, and for fertilizer. Vitamins are extracted from the one-ton liver. In a recent season, Antarctic whalers butchered 36,390 whales, taking 2,048,159 barrels of oil.

SPERM WHALE'S TEETH are tapped from its jaw. Although sperm teeth have little commercial value, the crewmen often ornament them by carving delicate designs called scrimshaw.

BLUBBER OF A BLUE WHALE (*left*) is cut up and shoveled down hatches to the boilers. The skeleton, as long as two boxcars, is also stewed into oil, which is pumped into a tanker for storage.

165

SLAUGHTERED PILOT WHALES (*above*) lie in a bay in the North Atlantic's Faeroe Islands. Each year, fishermen herd whales into the bay like sheep to kill them for food.

WHITE WHALES (*opposite*) gather in Hudson Bay to breed. Also called belugas, they are born black, turn white only at maturity. They squeak plaintively when harpooned.

ATOMIC SUBS, like the U.S.
Navy's *Nautilus*, have created
a new era in mankind's
relation to the sea. Nuclear
fuels have made man into a
marine creature, freed from the
land for months, traveling
untroubled in storm-free depths.

9

Man
and the Future
of the Sea

The seas are mankind's last frontier on this planet. For ages, islanders
that we are, we have treated the great waters as little more than
hunting grounds for fishermen, highways for ships. Now we are awakening to see that invisible beneath the waves lies a vast, virgin territory
every bit as challenging as outer space and infinitely more promising of
economic reward. Man at last has the scientific capability and technical
mastery to meet the challenge, and his growing need for food, water, minerals, power and weather control gives him solid reasons for doing so.

If man is to get more from the sea, however, he must start by obtaining
more knowledge of it. The International Geophysical Year, uniting scientists of 66 nations for the study of outer and "inner" space, enormously
advanced man's understanding of the earth and sea, and the advance has
continued ever since. In 1961, President Kennedy asked Congress to
double the amount of money the United States government has been
spending on ocean research. "Knowledge of the oceans is more than a
matter of curiosity," he said. "Our very survival may hinge on it."

As an outgrowth of this concentration of interest, United States scientists put into effect a venture as bold as anything Columbus imagined. Their purpose: nothing less than to drill a hole through the bottom of the sea to find out what the earth's interior is made of. This venture is Project Mohole, so named for the Mohorovičić discontinuity, or "Moho," a region marking the boundary between the earth's crust and the 1,800-mile-thick "plastic" layer surrounding our planet's core. Mohole is being dug in the sea rather than on the land because the earth's crust is not more than about three miles thick below the deep-ocean basins, whereas it is probably an average of 20 miles thick beneath the continents.

Mohole is a tough project; it will take years. But the scientists have already scored what President Kennedy has hailed as "a spectacular achievement." Using a chartered offshore oil-drilling rig, they first sank test holes in the bottom in 3,000 feet of water off San Diego. Having thus proved that it is possible to drill in deep water, they moved right out to sea off Guadalupe Island, near Lower California, and drilled five more test holes in 12,000 feet of water, one of them penetrating 601 feet through sediment and basalt, deeper than man had ever before probed under the sea.

Besides producing the deepest core samples ever taken, these tests triumphantly demonstrated that a drilling rig could be kept in place on the open sea well enough to carry on deep-drilling operations. Of course the Guadalupe Island tests were just a starter. A site for final drilling has yet to be picked. A far bigger rig will be needed, and the technical problem of sinking a casing in the earth's crust through which the drill will go all the way to the Moho has yet to be surmounted.

To gather more new facts from oceans, scientists are developing many instruments and techniques that will play a greater part in man's future in the sea. Some will be almost immediately useful. The mid-1960's should see the launching of vehicles that will not only be able to descend to the deepest abyss like the bathyscaphs but cruise about the ocean bottom as well. Scientists have also suggested a world-wide network of automatic underwater stations that will continuously record data on deep currents, temperatures, saltiness and other conditions on the sea floor, and flash sound-beam reports to ship and shore stations. They also foresee the use of acoustic beacons placed on the bottom to guide ships on their way. These will be an improvement over present radio aids now used for navigation, since they will be closer together and nearer ships at sea.

Some of the newest oceanographic instruments are aimed at helping us learn more about the sea's vital but still little understood effect on weather changes. We may find ourselves the beneficiaries of a world-wide system of radio buoys designed to record and transmit variations in ocean currents, for it is becoming clear that currents influence day-to-day weather in adjacent countries. In addition, hurricanes and typhoons will someday be tracked with earthquake recorders, or seismometers, left at the bottom of the sea. It has long been suspected that storms at sea transmit disturbances to the ocean floor, where they cause minute tremors in the earth's crust. Recently these tremors have been detected by seismometers dropped to the bottom. A network of these instruments, connected to shore stations by cable, would make it unnecessary to send planes out into howling storms —as must be done today—to plot their tracks.

Many oceanographers see in the seas not only a key to understanding and forecasting weather, but a means of directing it. A Soviet engineer has proposed building a 46-mile dam across the Bering Strait, then pumping out the cold Arctic water and replacing it with warmer Pacific water. This, he said, would not only clear the Soviet Union's 3,000-mile Arctic shoreline of ice but would greatly reduce the severity of winter storms and perhaps extend the tropics northward. Soviet and American writers have also proposed exploding nuclear bombs to melt the Arctic ice. But man will have to weigh all such schemes with the greatest care. If Ewing and Donn are right in their hypothesis of the recurrent ice ages, the melting of Arctic ice, far from covering Siberia with orange groves, would bring on another ice age that would cover not only Siberia with glaciers but a great many other places as well.

The most grandiose of oceanic dams so far dreamed up, however, is meant to keep the climate exactly as it is. Its author is Gail A. Hathaway, one of the select circle of engineers who designed the TVA, Grand Coulee and other mammoth dams. After reading about the Ewing-Donn ice-age theory, Hathaway proposed a dam that would extend 1,100 miles across the sea from Greenland to Norway, walling off the Arctic Ocean from the Atlantic. This would serve to halt the flow of warm Atlantic water into the Arctic that Ewing and Donn believe melted the Arctic floes and started the ice ages. Hathaway concedes that there is no need for the big dam yet, nor will there be so long as the Arctic stays solidly frozen.

None of these proposed oceanic dam schemes is aimed at harnessing the sea for power, although doing so has long been one of man's fondest dreams. Back in the 1930s the United States government actually set out to harness the great tides of the Bay of Fundy, starting to build a system of gates and dams at Passamaquoddy, Maine, designed for the generation of three billion kilowatts of electric power. At about the same time, Georges Claude, inventor of the neon light, spent a fortune on a scheme for turning a turbine by exploiting the wide difference in temperature between the ocean's cold bottom and the warm surface waters. The United States abandoned Passamaquoddy as too costly, and though the French government still talks about carrying through Claude's ideas, science may have leaped beyond its old dream of harnessing the sea since the advent of atomic power.

There seems little doubt that in the future man will turn to the sea for water. He will probably be compelled to. Even a country as plentifully blessed with rivers and lakes as the United States cannot increase its water consumption indefinitely. In 1960, the United States used 300 billion gallons of fresh water daily for its industrial, agricultural and human needs. This is 60 per cent of the 500 billion gallons a day that the United States Geological Survey says is readily available from natural resources. Much of the United States West has never had enough water. Many other countries are worse off.

Fresh water is distilled from sea water on many ships, but this process is too expensive for everyday use. It costs around $2 a thousand gallons

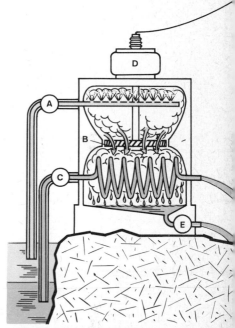

POWER FROM THE SEA is hoped for in an experimental plant which exploits temperature differences of sea water. Warm surface water is drawn by pump (A) to the top chamber; under partial vacuum it is vaporized and drawn to the lower chamber, turning the turbine (B) to produce power (generator, D). The temperature difference which helps make the vacuum is created by pumping cold deep water (C) into a coil. Condensed vapor is removed by a pump (E).

—four to eight times what most Americans pay for water. A much cheaper method is needed, and intensive research is now being carried out on three basic ways of separating the salt and water—by heating, by freezing and by driving the water through specially treated plastic membranes that pass water molecules but catch the salt. The United States is planning or building experimental plants which give promise of producing fresh water in quantity at seasides for as little as 50 cents a thousand gallons—not far above what many communities now pay for water.

In California, where water is the Number One community problem, the Scripps Institution's John Isaacs has suggested that icebergs be fetched up from the Antarctic to ease the local water shortage. Fantastic? Not at all, say oceanographer Isaacs' colleagues, who have made the calculations and found, somewhat to their astonishment, that this is one dreamboat that might really float. Being formed from glaciers, icebergs are completely salt-free. And unlike the smaller North Atlantic variety, Antarctic icebergs are big enough to make the idea worthwhile. A berg 10 miles long, a half mile wide and 600 feet thick is small for the Antarctic.

This is what the scientists' slide rules told them: in two months' time three ocean-going tugs could work a 10-mile-long, half-mile-wide berg into the Humboldt Current running up the west coast of South America. Where the Humboldt Current slows down off Peru and Ecuador, the tugs would steer the berg into other favoring currents that would lead it in a long, lateral loop almost to Hawaii and eventually to Los Angeles. The whole trip would take about a year and along the way the berg might lose as much as half its vast bulk. But it would still represent about 300 billion gallons of fresh water. Authorities could ground the berg on an offshore shoal and surround it with a floating dam extending about 20 feet or so below the surface. This would keep the fresh water penned in around the berg as the ice melted. Because it is lighter, the fresh water would stay on top of the salt water, and the city of Los Angeles could pump it out as needed through pipes leading to the mainland. One berg would be enough to supply the city's normal needs for about a month. The total cost of the water so delivered (mainly $1,000,000 for a year's hire of three ocean-going tugs) works out at something like one third of a cent per thousand gallons, a minute fraction of what Los Angeles now pays for its drinking water.

In the catalogue of what mankind may expect to take from the sea, one of the brightest items for the future is the ocean's great store of minerals. Though offshore drilling is in its infancy, the continental shelves off United States coasts already hold about 20 per cent of the country's proved oil and gas reserves lying in sediments below the sea floor. About 40 million square miles of ocean bottom consist of clays containing enough copper and

aluminum to supply man for a million years at present rates of consumption. Also conveniently located in shallow areas near shore are large beds of phosphorite, a mineral rich in phosphorus, from which chemical fertilizers are made. Then there are the manganese nodules mentioned in a previous chapter, which also contain cobalt, nickel and copper. In one part of the eastern Pacific, Scripps Institution scientists have found more than a million dollars' worth of nodules per square mile. John L. Mero and associates at the University of California believe that nodules can be marketed at a profit of $20 a ton.

O f all the sea's possibilities for man's future, the greatest may be its promise of a significant increase in the world's food supply. Square mile for square mile, the sea is estimated to be potentially more productive than the land. Yet at present the oceans supply only one or 2 per cent of man's food. Despite all he is learning about the sea, man's relationship to it is still primitive; he is a hunter rather than a harvester. Along some coasts oyster growers set out beds of oysters and fence out the oysters' enemies to increase the yield. In the Philippines, Indonesia, Japan and China, people already grow fish and prawns in fresh-water ponds. But this is just a beginning. In the future, to meet the vast needs of an exploding world population, man will have to start farming the sea as he has for so long farmed the land.

There are many things that can be done to increase the sea's yield of food. One was pioneered over a half century ago by the British biologist Walter Garstang, who transplanted young plaice, or European flounder, from their crowded shallows off the Dutch coast to a similar area, bare of plaice, in the middle of the North Sea. He did this several times and each time discovered that the transplanted plaice grew to three times the size of their brothers in the crowded Dutch waters. Striped bass, shad and soft-shelled clams have been successfully transplanted from the East to the West Coast of North America, and the North American Chinook salmon has been established in New Zealand.

In the aquaculture of the future, it should not be necessary to spread fertilizer in the sea as farmers do on land. But it may be useful to stimulate the flow of nutrients to those areas most conveniently accessible for sea farming. Columbus O'Donnell Iselin, dean of American oceanographers, suggests that we can induce upwellings of mineral-rich cold water along our coasts by using jet engines placed on shore or on big buoys to pump compressed air through long tubes to the deep-sea layers. The rising bubbles of air would carry nutrients up with them. Another Iselin idea is to cause an upwelling in the Gulf Stream by anchoring a quantity of submerged buoys across the Florida strait with huge otter boards attached to

A 10-MILE ICEBERG could be towed from Antarctica to Los Angeles as a cheap source of 300 billion gallons of fresh water. So say some scientists, who calculate that tugs could get the berg's speed up to two knots after a month. Then, maneuvering it into favorable currents, they could land it in California a year later—with only half its original bulk melted.

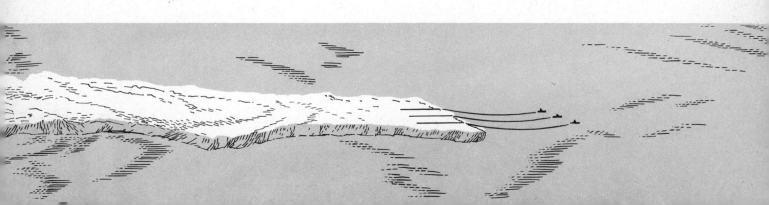

them deep in the water. Each of these planes would be tilted in such a way as to deflect the cold bottom waters upward. This, he predicts, would fetch nutrient minerals up to the top, turn the Gulf Stream off the southeastern United States green with blooming plankton and conceivably boom the fishing industry in the South Atlantic states.

When the time comes to farm the sea, says Sir Alister Hardy of Oxford, man will go under water to raise fish. As a first step he will have to make a distinction between creatures he can eat and those he cannot. The latter, says Sir Alister, will have to be classified as weeds and rooted out. As long ago as World War I a marine biologist calculated that "weeds"—i.e., inedible creatures like brittle stars and starfish—devour all but a tiny percentage of the fish food available in the sea. To clear away these weeds so that the fish can get at least 20 per cent of the available food, Professor Hardy expects that sea farmers "working in two hour shifts from a mother ship above . . . will be driving pressure-proof submarine tractors down below." Equipped with buoyancy tanks and driven by propellers, these submarine tractors will be able to skim the bottom in the growing season, raking off the starfish and other weeds. Later, when harvest time comes, the same tractors with their deep-sea drivers at the helm will whisk nets through the same waters and collect the fish that have grown fat on their unshared sea-bottom fare.

Sir Alister foresees such scenes in the coastal waters around Europe, but their adoption is probably something for the distant future. Europe is already quite well provided with food resources. Like the United States, whose requirements for sea food are expected to double in the next two decades, Europe can probably meet its own expanded needs in the future simply by improving present fishery methods. But for many countries in Asia, Africa and Latin America with exploding birth rates, survival may hinge on the development of some sort of intensive underwater farming. Pessimists predict that man will some day be forced to eat plankton. Though this always remains a possibility, there are two principal obstacles. In the first place, man is not nearly so efficient at collecting it as whales are, and this may well turn out to be prohibitively expensive. In the second, a good deal of it does not taste good.

Such are a few of the potentialities of the world's last great storehouse of wealth. Man has begun his assault on the sea, and he is certain to continue. But sometime in the future the sea itself must come to an end. Astronomers predict that the sun will pass through a "red giant" stage before turning into a cold, dark lump of matter drifting through space. This will not happen for at least three billion years—perhaps not for 10 billion years, or about twice as long as the earth and solar system have existed up to now. But when the sun does turn into a red giant, it will swell to nearly 100 times its present size, emitting immense quantities of heat in the process. In its baleful red light the earth's temperature will rise inexorably. Life will shrivel and the seas will boil away in clouds of steam. Some of this steam will escape into space, but the bulk of it will fall back to earth when the sun cools again. As the solar furnace burns lower and lower, what is left of the oceans will slowly freeze. In time they will become solid ice, and in this form they will endure as long as the earth itself endures.

Man Invades the Sea

AN UNDERSEA GEOLOGIST GATHERS SAND DOLLARS AND OTHER LIVING FOSSILS AS CLUES IN FINDING FOSSIL-BEARING OIL BEDS

With new knowledge and techniques which have become available only in the last decades, man is now beginning to tap undersea riches. Though his relationship to the sea is still that of primitive hunter rather than cultivator, he is on his way at last to exploiting it for food, water, minerals and control of his climate.

IN THE SUNSET NEAR WELIGAMA ON CEYLON'S SOUTHERN COAST, FISHERMEN STAND ON STILTS IN THE SURF, CASTING LINES FOR

Food from the Sea

Some 40 million tons of fish are taken annually from the sea, but men still search out and capture the game rather than raise it, although they have been raising plants and animals on land for 7,000 years. The stilt fishermen of the southern Ceylon coast and the sonar-guided purse-seiners of the U.S. Carolina coast are both essentially hunters; the only difference between them is in efficiency. The Ceylonese eke out a primitive living casting lines for sardines and other small fish from stilts sunk in the sand. The ultramodern U.S. menhaden-catching industry uses planes to spot schools, radio telephones to direct the boats and an electronic fishfinder to fix the school's exact depth.

The next step for man is to start gardening the sea, planting the young fry, weeding out bottom pests such as starfish that eat up vital food, and then reaping the fattened crop (perhaps with the aid of undersea tractors). Then the new age will begin: the age of aquaculture.

SARDINES, A TECHNIQUE UNCHANGED FOR MANY CENTURIES

SONAR SIGNALS, obtained by bouncing sound waves off undersea objects, show the sea bottom as a long black line on the finder, two schools of fish as smudges (*far right*).

NET IS TIGHTENED around a school of menhaden by two net layers (*lower right*) as a parent boat comes to get the catch. The other boats prepare their own purse nets.

177

RADAR REFLECTOR

RADAR ANTENNA

LUBRICATING HOSE

CASING RACK

ROTARY TABLE

CENTER WELL

SONAR RECEIVING EQUIPMENT

CONTROL UNIT

CORE LAB

CUSS I

OUTBOARD MOTOR

GUIDE SHOE DRILL PIPE

A Hole in the Ocean Bottom

Aboard the odd vessel shown above, U.S. scientists in 1961 drilled a hole to the earth's interior through the ocean floor. Boring in 11,672 feet of water off Lower California, they drove a record 601 feet into the bottom and proved that such deep drilling is feasible in the open sea. Project Mohole, so called for the Mohorovičić discontinuity, or "Moho," the region where the earth's light crust meets the more plastic mass beneath, is being carried out at sea because there the Moho is only three miles below the floor; on land it lies a drill-busting 20 to 40 miles down through solidified rock. The drillers did not reach the Moho this time but expect to in a few years, using a larger vessel and profiting by the lessons of this probe. Meanwhile, they have taken 20-million-year-old fossils from the deepest core samplings of bottom sediments ever brought up. Scientists also hope to answer a puzzle: what happened to all the mud? Estimates of continental erosion show that the deep ocean bottom should have an average of at least 16,400 feet of sediments, but the average is only 1,640 feet. Where is the rest—dissolved in sea water or changed into rock? Moho may give an answer.

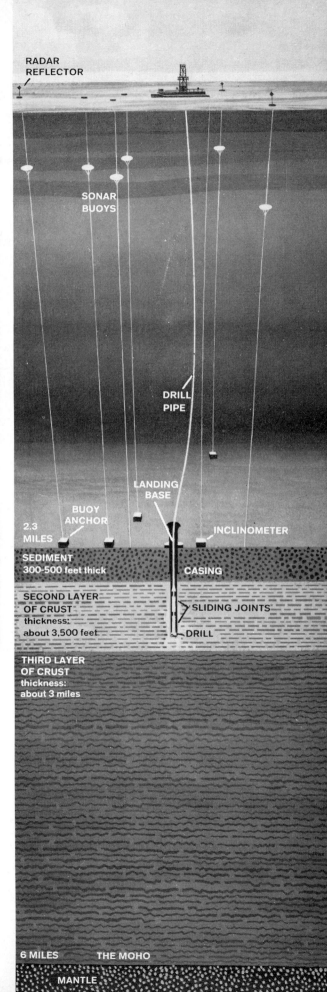

MOHOLE CRAFT is a converted oil-drilling barge named *Cuss I*. The man in the control unit steadies it over the hole in the sea bed by slowing or speeding four big outboard motors. Drill-pipe sections are lowered through a guide shoe, which protects them if the boat rocks.

"CUSS I" IS KEPT ON STATION with the help of three anchored radar-reflector buoys on the surface of the water. These appear as a pattern on a radar screen in the control unit. The pilot runs his four outboard motors to keep *Cuss I* squarely in the center of the pattern. In addition, he has three sonar buoys 200 feet down. A landing base on the ocean floor keeps the long pipe shaft from bending too far under the stress of deep currents. Just above the diamond-studded drill tip itself are two sliding joints that act as shock absorbers when the drill hits bottom. Sea water pumped down the pipe cools the drill, and coring tubes are sent down to bring back earth samples. As the bit cuts through the bottom sediment, sections of steel casing are lowered around the pipe shaft to keep the sides of the hole from caving in.

Mineral Treasure Lies Waiting on the Floor of the Sea

Vast bottom areas of the ocean are strewn with mysteriously formed nodules containing an average of 25 per cent manganese, 15 per cent iron and small quantities of cobalt, nickel and copper. Some concentrations are worth up to $10 million a square mile. John L. Mero of the University of California proposes collecting the lumps with gigantic vacuum-cleanerlike hydraulic dredges (*sketch at right*). As the rig moved gradually, extension pipes with suction heads would snuff up the lumps, and pumps would lift them up through as much as three miles of pipe into a barge. The extracted metal would yield an estimated $20-a-ton profit.

MANGANESE NODULES on the sea bed, 18,000 feet down, were viewed by a Russian IGY camera. A shark's tooth or whale's ear bone may form the nucleus of a nodule.

NODULE COLLECTOR that is proposed by oceanographer John L. Mero has propellers, gyros and floats to keep the pipe positioned, and TV cameras to find nodules.

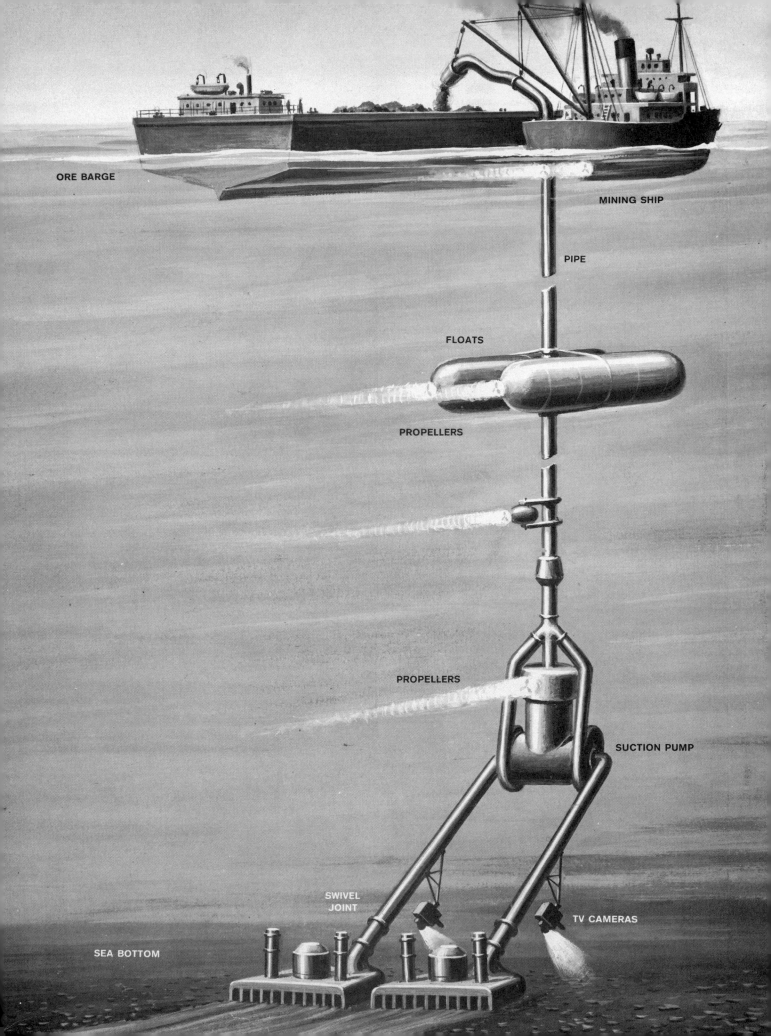

ORE BARGE

MINING SHIP

PIPE

FLOATS

PROPELLERS

PROPELLERS

SUCTION PUMP

SWIVEL JOINT

TV CAMERAS

SEA BOTTOM

Appendix

IMPORTANT HISTORICAL DATES

B.C.

c. 2000-1000 Phoenicians, world's first seafarers, explore the Mediterranean, the shores of the Red Sea, Somaliland, Arabia, Indian, perhaps China, and discover the Canary and Scilly Islands.

c. 590 Egyptian monarch Necho dispatches Phoenicians on the first great recorded voyage in history: the circumnavigation of Africa.

c. 400 The three major continents of Europe, "Libya" and Asia are depicted washed by three great oceans—Mare Atlanticum, Mare Australis and Mare Erythraeum—on a map by Herodotus.

c. 325 Greek astronomer-geographer Pytheas makes the first great scientific voyage of marine exploration. Sailing north to Iceland, he uses astronomical measurements to work out a way of determining latitude and proposes the idea that tidal movements are influenced by the moon.

c. 100 Stoic philosopher Posidonius undertakes a scientific voyage to Spain to determine whether the sun hisses when setting in the Atlantic. He makes the first reference to deep sounding as he records depth of sea near Sardinia as 1,000 fathoms and takes measurements of Atlantic tides.

A.D.

127-141 Ptolemy evolves a theory of the universe with the earth as a sphere, making the most significant contribution to oceanography until the Age of Exploration.

914 Arabian historian-geographer Masudi records accurate principles about evaporation, the formation of rain and causes of ocean salinity.

c. 1003 Viking Leif Erickson crosses the Atlantic to "Vinland," makes the first landfall on North America.

1100 First recorded mention of European use of the magnetic needle as a mariner's guide.

c. 1100-1300 Polynesians navigating by stars and bird migrations explore the Pacific, colonizing the Hawaiian Islands, the Solomons and New Zealand.

1292 After 17 years in China, Marco Polo returns to Europe with fleet of 14 ships traveling via Sumatra, Ceylon and Persia to Venice.

1416 Prince Henry of Portugal founds a school of navigation at Sagres and launches the great age of maritime exploration.

1488 Bartholomew Diaz sails around the southern tip of Africa, becoming the first man to enter the Indian Ocean from the west.

1492 Christopher Columbus sets out to find western sea route to India, makes landfalls in America, which he thinks is the easternmost fringe of Asia.

1499-1501 Amerigo Vespucci explores 6,000 miles of South American coastline. He also evolves a system for computing nearly exact longitude, and arrives at a figure for the earth's equatorial circumference only 50 miles short of the correct measurement.

1513 Vasco Nuñez de Balboa makes a land crossing from Panama and becomes the first European to view the Pacific Ocean.

1519 Ferdinand Magellan sets out to find Asia by sailing around the tip of South America. In the Philippines, he and most of his crew are killed, but Juan del Cano crosses the Indian Ocean and completes the first circumnavigation of the globe.

1576 Martin Frobisher attempts to find the Northwest Passage to the Orient via the Arctic.

1585 Gerardus Mercator, having devised maps using projections, starts compiling a great atlas of maps of the world.

1594 Dutch navigator William Barents makes three unsuccessful attempts to find a Northeast Passage to India, discovers Spitsbergen.

1609 Henry Hudson, on continuing search for northern passage, sails up the Hudson River, later sails through the Hudson Straits into Hudson Bay.

1616 William Baffin, sailing through Baffin Bay, becomes convinced an ice-free Northwest Passage does not exist.

1642 Dutchman Abel Tasman circumnavigates Australia, proving it is not part of the southern continent, also discovers Tasmania and New Zealand.

1687 Isaac Newton establishes the relationship of ocean tidal movement to the moon.

1737 Most fearful destruction by seismic waves on record occurs in the Bay of Bengal when 300,000 persons are killed and 20,000 boats destroyed.

1768-1776 Captain James Cook, sailing on the *Endeavour*, makes the first modern expedition of scientific ocean exploration. In a series of voyages he delimits the whole of the world's largest ocean and becomes the first man to cross the Antarctic Circle. He is the first to take subsurface ocean temperatures, also measures winds and currents, charts South Pacific islands, takes soundings and collects important facts about coral reefs.

1769 Deputy Postmaster General of the Colonies Benjamin Franklin uses temperature measurements and observation of water color to track the Gulf Stream, and devises the first chart for navigators.

1772 French chemist Antoine Lavoisier makes earliest quantitative analyses of sea water.

1795 British Admiralty begins a survey of coasts of the world, a forerunner of the modern Admiralty pilots.

1790-1830 English geographer James Rennell pioneers in the scientific study of winds and currents, making the first comprehensive study of Atlantic Ocean currents.

1802 Launching the modern era of navigation, Nathaniel Bowditch publishes *The American Practical Navigator*, while the British devise the first seagoing chronometer.

1818 Sir John Ross devises a "deep sea clamm" to bring up mud deposits in which worms are found, from depth of 1,000 fathoms, revealing the existence of animal life in the ocean bed.

1837 Charles Darwin proposes his theory on coral reefs.

1841 Edward Forbes pioneers in the use of a dredge in the scientific study of shallow water. Considered the father of marine biology and, along with Matthew Maury (*see below*), a co-founder of the science of oceanography, he is one of the first men to think of the sea as an entity and to divide the ocean into natural zones on scientific grounds.

1845 Sir John Franklin, seeking a Northwest Passage, is lost. Rescue ships coming from east and west meet in Melville Sound and the Northwest Passage is found.

1855 American Lieutenant Matthew Maury publishes the first textbook and classic of oceanography, *The Physical Geography of the Sea*. Concerned with the physical and mechanical aspects of sea science, Maury spends years compiling all available records on winds, currents and temperatures from ships' logs, and publishes the first chart of the depths of the Atlantic.

1864 Norwegian Svend Foyn invents the harpoon gun and modern whaling industry begins.

1866 German biologist Ernst Haeckel divides sea organisms by habitat into two groups: nekton (organisms of the open ocean) and benthos (organisms of the sea bottom). German physiologist Viktor Hensen later adds a third group: plankton, or non-free-swimming organisms.

1872 Anton Dohrn founds first marine biological center in Naples to study marine life, spurring other nations to start oceanographical institutes.

1872-1876 The age of modern oceanography begins as the *Challenger* expedition led by Sir Charles Wyville Thomson travels 69,000 miles around the globe, sailing in every ocean but the Arctic. The expedition takes hundreds of soundings, dredges the ocean floor for marine life, analyzes sea water, classifies sediments and studies currents.

1879 Swedish Baron A. E. Nordenskjöld locates the Northeast Passage to the Pacific when he sails from Norway through the Bering Strait to Japan.

1883 The greatest seismic explosion in modern times occurs at Krakatoa when eruptions wipe out an island 1,400 feet above sea level and kill 36,380 persons.

1893-1896 Norwegian explorer Fridtjof Nansen deliberately lets his ship, the *Fram*, freeze in the polar icecap to prove the existence of the Arctic Ocean and nonexistence of land.

1903 Norwegian explorer Roald Amundsen becomes the first man to negotiate the Northwest Passage.

1909 Admiral Robert Peary reaches the North Pole.

1911 Roald Amundsen reaches the South Pole.

1924 F. A. Vening Meinesz of the Netherlands makes first gravity measurements at sea, using a pendulum device in a submarine.

1927 Sir Hubert Wilkins takes the deepest sounding in the Arctic Sea at 17,850 feet, and later unsuccessfully attempts to travel beneath the ice under the North Pole in the submarine *Nautilus*.

1934 Otis Barton and William Beebe reach a depth of 3,028 feet in a bathysphere.

1937 Dr. Maurice Ewing develops seismic shooting.

1945 Swedish oceanographer Börje Kullenberg develops a piston corer which sucks up cores 65 feet long from the ocean floor.

1947 Dr. Harold Urey develops an "oxygen thermometer" to measure isotope ratios in sediments and determine ancient climate. Dr. Willard Libby subsequently develops "atomic clock" to determine the chronology of ice ages from ice cores.

1947 Dr. Maurice Ewing starts systematic mapping of topography of the North Atlantic sea floor using modern deep-sea sounder and discovers an abyssal plain over 200 miles wide in deepest part of the Atlantic.

1947 Swedish Deep Sea Expedition explores Atlantic Ocean bed and, finding extreme ruggedness, disproves theories about the flatness of the ocean bottom. Hans Pettersson takes measurements in Atlantic basin and finds sediment layers as much as 12,000 feet thick.

1950-1952 Danish Deep Sea Expedition retrieves mud samples from record depth of 33,017 feet in the Philippine Trench, proving presence of organisms in the deepest ocean trenches, also captures the Neopilina, presumably extinct for some 350 million years.

1950-1957 Scripps Institution of Oceanography takes 300,-000 soundings in program to map the Pacific floor.

1950 Perfection of the aqualung permits geologists to explore shallow margins of the ocean in water depths less than 200 feet. Jacques Cousteau uses the aqualung for the exploration of continental shelves.

1952 First large-scale investigation of coral reefs is undertaken by U. S. Task Force I in preparation for bomb tests. Boring through Eniwetok, scientists come up with volcanic rock, confirming Darwin's 1837 theory on the formation of coral reefs.

1956 Existence of longest submarine mountain range in world, the Mid-Ocean Ridge, running 40,000 miles, is predicted, and confirmed during next four years.

1957-1958 International Geophysical Year is proclaimed. Research aims in oceanography are to study: the use of ocean depths for the dumping of radioactive wastes, the protein potential in the ocean for sustaining the population explosion, and the role of the oceans in climate change. The Special Committee on Oceanographic Research coordinates the work, setting up 30 stations in the Atlantic, Pacific and Indian Oceans and using 80 research ships to make a hydrographic survey of the Atlantic.

1958 U.S. submarine *Nautilus* sails under the ice to the North Pole.

1960 Jacques Piccard and Don Walsh make a record-breaking 35,800-foot descent to the bottom of the Mariana Trench in the bathyscaph *Trieste*, designed by Piccard's father, Auguste Piccard.

1961 U.S. scientist Willard Bascom directs first drilling tests for Project Mohole.

GREAT OCEANS AND SEAS

	AREA (SQ. MI.)	DEPTH IN FEET AVERAGE	DEPTH IN FEET GREATEST		AREA (SQ. MI.)	DEPTH IN FEET AVERAGE	DEPTH IN FEET GREATEST
Pacific Ocean	63,985,000	14,040	35,630	Okhotsk, Sea of	580,000	3,000	12,621
Atlantic Ocean	31,529,000	12,880	27,510	East China Sea	480,000	610	8,920
Indian Ocean	28,357,000	13,000	24,444	Yellow Sea	480,000	160	348
Arctic Ocean	5,541,000	4,200	17,500	Hudson Bay	472,000	440	849
Mediterranean Sea	1,145,000	4,500	15,072	Japan, Sea of	405,000	4,835	13,241
South China Sea	895,000	5,400	16,456	North Sea	221,000	180	2,165
Bering Sea	878,000	1,665	13,420	Red Sea	178,000	1,490	9,301
Caribbean Sea	750,000	8,400	23,750	Black Sea	168,500	4,300	7,362
Gulf of Mexico	700,000	4,700	12,426	Baltic Sea	158,000	221	1,400

PRINCIPAL LAKES

	AREA (SQ. MI.)		AREA (SQ. MI.)		AREA (SQ. MI.)
*Caspian, Soviet Union-Iran	152,123	Chad, Chad-Niger	8,000	Winnipegosis, Canada	2,086
Superior, U.S.-Canada	31,820	Ontario, U.S.-Canada	7,540	Bangweulu, Northern Rhodesia	2,000
Victoria, Kenya-Uganda-Tanganyika	26,828	Ladoga, Soviet Union	7,104	*Urmia, Iran	1,900
*Aral, Soviet Union	26,525	Balkhash, Soviet Union	6,680	Manitoba, Canada	1,817
Huron, U.S.-Canada	23,010	Onega, Soviet Union	3,822	Albert, Uganda-The Congo	1,750
Michigan, U.S.	22,400	*Eyre, Australia	3,700	*Great Salt, U.S.	1,700
Tanganyika, Tanganyika-The Congo	12,355	*Rudolf, Kenya	3,500	Leopold II, The Congo	1,700
Baykal, Soviet Union	12,162	Titicaca, Peru-Bolivia	3,261	Khanka, Soviet Union-China	1,699
Great Bear, Canada	12,000	Nicaragua, Nicaragua	3,060	Dubawnt, Canada	1,650
Great Slave, Canada	11,170	Athabasca, Canada	3,058	Nipigon, Canada	1,640
Nyasa, Nyasaland	10,900	Reindeer, Canada	2,440	*Gairdner, Australia	1,500
Erie, U.S.-Canada	9,940	*Torrens, Australia	2,400	Lake of the Woods, U.S.-Canada	1,500
Winnipeg, Canada	9,094	*Ching Hai (Koko Nor), China	2,300	*Van, Turkey	1,450
		Issyk-Kul, Soviet Union	2,200		
		Vänern, Sweden	2,150		

*Salt lakes

PRINCIPAL RIVERS

	LENGTH (MILES)		LENGTH (MILES)		LENGTH (MILES)
Nile, Africa	4,132	Salween, Asia	1,730	Snake, North America	1,038
Amazon, South America	3,900	Euphrates, Asia	1,675	Uruguay, South America	1,025
Mississippi-Missouri-Red Rock, North America	3,860	Syr Darya, Asia	1,653	Red, North America	1,018
Ob-Irtysh, Asia	3,461	Zambezi, Africa	1,650	Churchill, North America	1,000
Yangtze, Asia	3,430	Tocantins, South America	1,640	Marañón, South America	1,000
Hwang Ho (Yellow), Asia	2,903	Araguaia, South America	1,630	Ohio, North America	981
Congo, Africa	2,900	Amu Darya, Asia	1,628	Magdalena, South America	950
Amur, Asia	2,802	Kolyma, Asia	1,615	Roosevelt (River of Doubt), South America	950
Lena, Asia	2,653	Murray, Australia	1,600	Godavari, Asia	930
Mackenzie, North America	2,635	Angara, Asia	1,550	Si, Asia	930
Mekong, Asia	2,600	Ganges, Asia	1,550	Oka, Europe	920
Niger, Africa	2,590	Pilcomayo, South America	1,550	Canadian, North America	906
Yenisey, Asia	2,566	Ural, Asia	1,522	Dnestr, Europe	876
Missouri, North America	2,466	Vilyuy, Asia	1,513	Brazos, North America	870
Paraná, South America	2,450	Arkansas, North America	1,450	Salado, South America	870
Mississippi, North America	2,330	Colorado, North America	1,450	Fraser, North America	850
Irtysh, Asia	2,300	Irrawaddy, Asia	1,425	Parnaíba, South America	850
La Plata-Paraguay, South America	2,300	Dnepr, Europe	1,420	Colorado, North America	840
Volga, Europe	2,293	Aldan, Asia	1,392	Rhine, Europe	820
Ob, Asia	2,260	Negro, South America	1,305	Narbada, Asia	800
Madeira, South America	2,060	Paraguay, South America	1,290	Athabasca, North America	765
Indus, Asia	1,980	Kama, Europe	1,261	Donets, Europe	735
Purús, South America	1,900	Xingú, South America	1,230	Pecos, North America	735
St. Lawrence, North America	1,900	Don, Europe	1,224	Green, North America	730
Rio Grande, North America	1,885	Ucayali, South America	1,220	Elbe, Europe	720
Brahmaputra, Asia	1,800	Columbia, North America	1,214	James, North America	710
Orinoco, South America	1,800	Saskatchewan, North America	1,205	Ottawa, North America	696
São Francisco, South America	1,800	Juruá, South America	1,200	White, North America	690
Yukon, North America	1,800	Peace, North America	1,195	Cumberland, North America	687
Danube, Europe	1,770	Orange, Africa	1,155	Gambia, Africa	680
Darling, Australia	1,750	Tigris, Asia	1,150	Yellowstone, North America	671
		Pechora, Europe	1,118	Tennessee, North America	652
		Dvina, Europe	1,100	Gila, North America	630
		Tobol, Asia	1,093	Vistula, Europe	630

Bibliography

Adventure and Exploration

Bruun, Anton F., Sv. Greve, Hakon Mielche and Ragnar Spärck, *The Galathea Deep Sea Expedition.* Macmillan, 1956.

Coppleson, V. M., *Shark Attack.* Angus & Robertson, London, 1959.

*Cousteau, Captain Jacques-Yves, with Frédéric Dumas, *The Silent World.* Harper & Brothers, 1953.

Darwin, Charles, *The Voyage of the Beagle.* E. P. Dutton.

Debenham, Frank, *Discovery and Exploration.* Doubleday, 1960.

Dugan, James, *Man Under the Sea.* Harper & Brothers, 1956.

Piccard, Auguste, *Earth, Sky and Sea.* Oxford University Press, 1956.

Fish and Fisheries

Hardy, Alister C., *The Open Sea.* (Vol. I, *The World of Plankton*, 1956; Vol. II, *Fish and Fisheries*, 1959). Houghton Mifflin.

Herald, Earl S., *Living Fishes of the World.* Doubleday, 1961.

Jordan, David Starr, *A Guide to the Study of Fishes* (2 vols.). Henry Holt, 1905.

Norman, J. R., and F. C. Fraser, *Field Book of Giant Fishes.* G. P. Putnam's Sons, 1949.

Schultz, Leonard P., with Edith M. Stern, *The Ways of Fishes.* D. Van Nostrand, 1948.

Zim, Herbert S., and Hurst H. Shoemaker, *Fishes.* Golden Press, 1956.

Geology and Oceanography

Barnes, H., *Oceanography and Marine Biology.* Macmillan, 1959.

Bascom, Willard, *A Hole in the Bottom of the Sea.* Doubleday, 1961.

Bigelow, Henry B., and W. T. Edmonson, *Wind Waves at Sea, Breakers and Surf.* Hydrographic Office Pub. No. 602, U.S. Government Printing Office, 1947.

Dunbar, Carl O., *Historical Geology* (rev. ed.). John Wiley & Sons, 1960.

Jacobs, J. A., R. D. Russell and J. Tuzo Wilson, *Physics and Geology.* McGraw-Hill, 1959.

Pettersson, Hans, *The Ocean Floor.* Yale University Press, 1954.

Sears, Mary, ed., *Oceanography.* American Association for the Advancement of Science, 1961.

Shepard, Francis P., *The Earth Beneath the Sea.* Johns Hopkins Press, 1959.

Invertebrates

Buchsbaum, Ralph, *Animals Without Backbones* (rev. ed.). University of Chicago Press, 1948.

Buchsbaum, Ralph, and Lorus J. Milne (in collaboration with Mildred Buchsbaum and Margery Milne), *The Lower Animals.* Doubleday, 1960.

Hyman, Libbie H., *The Invertebrates* (5 vols.). McGraw-Hill, 1940-1959.

Mammals

Bourlière, François, *The Natural History of Mammals* (rev. ed.). Alfred A. Knopf, 1960.

Budker, Paul, *Whales and Whaling.* Macmillan, 1959.

Colbert, Edwin Harris, *Evolution of the Vertebrates.* John Wiley & Sons, 1955.

Romer, Alfred S., *The Vertebrate Story.* University of Chicago Press, 1959. Original version: †*Man and the Vertebrates.*

Sanderson, Ivan T., *Follow the Whale.* Little, Brown, 1956. *Living Mammals of the World.* Hanover House, 1955.

The Shore and the Shallows

*Berrill, N. J., *The Living Tide.* Dodd, Mead, 1951.

Berrill, N. J., and Jacquelyn Berrill, *1001 Questions Answered About the Seashore.* Dodd, Mead, 1959.

*Carson, Rachel L., *The Edge of the Sea.* Houghton Mifflin, 1955.

Miner, Roy Waldo, *Field Book of Seashore Life.* G. P. Putnam's Sons, 1950.

Ricketts, Edward F., and Jack Calvin, *Between Pacific Tides.* Stanford University Press, 1939.

Wilson, D. P., *Life of the Shore and Shallow Sea.* Nicholson and Watson, London, 1951.

Zim, Herbert S., and Lester Ingle, *Seashores.* Golden Press, 1955.

General

Augusta, Joseph, and Zdeněk Burian, *Prehistoric Animals.* Spring Books, London.

*Bates, Marston, *The Forest and the Sea.* Random House, 1960.

Buzzati-Traverso, A. A., ed., *Perspectives in Marine Biology.* University of California Press, 1960.

Carrington, Richard, *A Biography of the Sea.* Basic Books, 1960. *Mermaids and Mastodons.* Rinehart, 1957.

*Carson, Rachel L., *The Sea Around Us* (rev. ed.). Oxford University Press, 1961.

Coker, R. E., *This Great and Wide Sea.* University of North Carolina Press, 1947.

Cowen, Robert C., *Frontiers of the Sea.* Doubleday, 1960.

*Defant, Albert, *Ebb and Flow: The Tides of Earth, Air and Water.* University of Michigan Press, 1958.

Douglas, John Scott, *The Story of the Oceans.* Dodd, Mead, 1952.

Drimmer, Frederick, ed., *The Animal Kingdom* (3 vols.). Garden City Books, 1954.

Halstead, Bruce W., *Dangerous Marine Animals.* Cornell Maritime Press, 1959.

Life Editorial Staff and Lincoln Barnett, *The World We Live In.* Time Inc., 1955.

MacGinitie, George E., and N. MacGinitie, *Natural History of Marine Animals.* McGraw-Hill, 1949.

Marshall, N. B., *Aspects of Deep Sea Biology.* Hutchinson, London, 1954.

Marshall, S. M., and A. P. Orr, eds., *Essays in Marine Biology.* Oliver & Boyd, Edinburgh & London, 1953.

Ray, Carleton, and Elgin Ciampi, *The Underwater Guide to Marine Life.* A. S. Barnes, 1956.

Romanovsky, V., Claude Francis-Boeuf, and Jacques Bourcart, *La Mer.* Librairie Larousse, Paris, 1953.

Russell, Frederick Stratten, and Charles Maurice Yonge, *The Seas: Our Knowledge of Life in the Sea and How It Is Gained.* Frederick Warne, London, 1928.

Simpson, George Gaylord, Colin S. Pittendrigh and Lewis H. Tiffany, *Life: An Introduction to Biology.* Harcourt, Brace, 1957.

Sverdrup, H. U., Martin W. Johnson and Richard H. Fleming, *The Oceans: Their Physics, Chemistry and General Biology.* Prentice-Hall, 1942.

Walford, Lionel A., *Living Resources of the Sea.* The Ronald Press, 1958.

* Also available in paperback edition.

† Only available in paperback edition.

Credits

The sources for the illustrations in this book are shown below. Credits for pictures from left to right are separated by commas, top to bottom by dashes.

Cover—Harry Pederson

8,9—Carola Gregor

10—Culver Pictures

12—Courtesy The New York Public Library—Culver Pictures

13—The Bettmann Archive

15—Drawing by Kenneth Gosner of the Newark Museum and Mark Binn

16—Drawing by Kenneth Gosner of the Newark Museum—Lennart Nilsson

17—George G. Lower, Dr. Thomas F. Goreau—drawing by Kenneth Gosner of the Newark Museum, Carleton Ray-Bahamas National Trust

18—Dr. Douglas P. Wilson

19—Drawing by Kenneth Gosner of the Newark Museum—Dr. Thomas F. Goreau, M. Woodbridge Williams

20,21—Tom Hutchins from Black Star, drawing by Kenneth Gosner of the Newark Museum—Keith Gillett, George G. Lower, Dr. Douglas P. Wilson

22—M. Woodbridge Williams

23—Keith Gillett, drawings by Kenneth Gosner of the Newark Museum—bottom right George Lower

24,25,26—Painting by Rudolf Freund

27,28,29—Drawing by Kenneth Gosner of the Newark Museum—painting by Rudolf Freund

30—Tom Hutchins from Black Star

31—Harold E. Edgerton

32,33—Henry G. Young except bottom left Wide World

34,35—Dr. Roman Vishniac—Fritz Goro, Tom Hutchins from Black Star

36—Martin F. Glaessner

40,43—Drawings by Matt Greene

44,45—G. F. Sternberg—Fort Hays Kansas State College Museum

46—Ward's Natural Science Establishment—Andreas Feininger

47 through 53—*Prehistoric Animals* published by Paul Hamlyn

54—Conrad Limbaugh

56 through 61—drawings by Jim Egleson

62—Official U.S. Navy Photo

63—David M. Owen

64 through 71—Kenneth Fagg

72,73—Kenneth Fagg (2), Phil Bath for TIME—John Launois from Black Star

74—Laurence R. Lowry from Rapho-Guillumette

76,77—Drawings by Jim Egleson except top left Matt Greene

80—Drawing by Matt Greene

81—Werner Wolff from Black Star

82,83—Antonio Petruccelli from model by Majorie Kirk Ulbrich, J. Alex Langley

84,85—Dr. Robert Cushman Murphy

86,87—M. Woodbridge Williams

88 through 91—Drawings by Matt Greene

93—Carola Gregor

94—Canadian National Railways—Dr. Francis P. Shepard—United Press International

95—Edward Rowe Snow

96,97—Eliot Elisofon, Dr. Roman Vishniac, M. Woodbridge Williams—Dr. Francis P. Shepard (2)

98—Fritz Goro

99—Robert W. L. Potts

100,101—Ewing Krainin from Photo Researchers, Fritz Goro—Dr. Douglas P. Wilson

102—Lennart Nilsson

105 through 111—Drawings by Kenneth Gosner of the Newark Museum

113 through 117—Lennart Nilsson

118—Jerry Greenberg

119,120,121—Dr. Roman Vishniac

122—Harold G. Cogger—Fritz Goro

123—Harry Pederson

124,125—Russ Kinne from Photo Researchers—Fritz Goro, Harry Pederson

126,127—Fritz Goro

128,129—Dr. Roman Vishniac, Fritz Goro—Lennart Nilsson

130—Russ Kinne from Photo Researchers

133,134,135—Drawings by Kenneth Gosner of the Newark Museum

137—Coles Weston

138—Peter Stackpole

139—Painting by C. E. Monroe Jr.

140,141—Painting by Richard Harker

142—Mort Beebe of Globecombers from D.P.I.

143—Ron Church

144,145—Hans Hass

147,148—Drawings by Kenneth Gosner of the Newark Museum

151—Karl W. Kenyon

152—Peter Stackpole

153—Robert Lackenbach

154,155—Michel Angot, John Phillips

156,157—Drawings by Rudolf Freund

158,159—Peter Stackpole

160 through 165—D. Richard Statile

166—Raymond Kleboe from Pix

167—Fritz Goro

168—Ralph Morse

171,172,173—Drawings by Matt Greene

176,177—Dmitri Kessel—Hank Walker, James H. Porterfield

178,179—Drawings by Adolph E. Brotman

180—Courtesy Dr. N. L. Zenkevitch

181—Drawing by Ray Pioch

Acknowledgments

The editors of this book are particularly indebted to these authorities: Maurice Ewing, Higgins Professor of Geology and Director, Lamont Geological Observatory, Columbia University, New York; and Ross F. Nigrelli, Professor of Biology, New York University, and Director, Laboratory of Marine Biology, New York Zoological Society. Both read the entire book and criticized the chapters in their own areas of study. The editors are also indebted to Francis P. Shepard, Professor of Submarine Geology, Scripps Institution of Oceanography, University of California; J. B. Hersey, Associate Professor of Oceanography, Massachusetts Institute of Technology, and Geophysicist, Woods Hole Oceanographic Institution; Norman D. Newell, Professor of Geology, Columbia University, and Curator, Invertebrate Fossils and Historical Geology, American Museum of Natural History; and Perry W. Gilbert, Professor of Zoology, Cornell University, Ithaca, New York.

Index

Numerals in italics indicate a photograph or painting of the subject mentioned.

xxx

Printed by R. R. Donnelley & Sons Company, Crawfordsville, Indiana, and Livermore and Knight Co., Providence, Rhode Island
Bound by R. R. Donnelley & Sons Company, Crawfordsville, Indiana
Paper by The Mead Corporation, Dayton, Ohio, and Crocker, Burbank Papers Inc., Fitchburg, Massachusetts